YOUR FUTURE IN AGRICULTURE

YOUR FUTURE
IN
AGRICULTURE

CHESTER S. HUTCHISON

RICHARDS ROSEN PRESS, INC., NEW YORK 10010

Library of Congress Catalog Card Number: 65-17017
Dewey Decimal Classification: 371.42

Published in 1965 by Richards Rosen Press, Inc.
29 East 21st Street, New York City, New York 10010

Manufactured in the United States of America

Revised Edition

About the Author

CHESTER S. HUTCHISON has had an outstanding career as an educator in the science of agriculture. Born in Ashville, Ohio, he was educated at The Ohio State University in Columbus, where he received a Bachelor of Science degree in agriculture and a Master of Arts degree in school administration, agricultural education, and principles of education.

In 1930 he joined the staff of the Ohio Department of Education, serving as district supervisor of vocational agriculture. Thereafter he became a member of the faculty of The Ohio State University as a teacher trainer and assistant professor of agricultural education (1936-40) and successively as junior dean, associate dean, and assistant dean. In the last-named capacity he taught a survey course on agriculture, counseled students and graduates in placement and Selective Service problems, directed short-course and conference programs, and selected recipients for scholarships in agriculture. He is now retired as Assistant Dean Emeritus.

Throughout his career he has been particularly interested in helping young people toward careers in agriculture. His activities in this area have included work with 4-H Clubs, Parent-Teacher Associations, the Future Farmers of America, the Young Farmer Association, and the Ohio Vocational Association. In Worthington, Ohio, where he makes his home, he has served as president of the Parent-Teachers Association, the Civic Association, and the Worthington Development Commission, and as mayor of the village—which reached the status of city during his term of office.

He has also been chairman of the Agricultural Careers Committee of the Association of Land Grant Colleges and Universities, a member of the Governor's Committee on Highway Safety for Ohio, and president of the Ohio Farm and Home Safety Committee.

Not the least among his varied interests is his own farm of four hundred fifty acres.

5

Contents

Preface

Introduction   11

    I. *Choosing a Career*   15
   II. *The Character of Modern Agriculture*   21
  III. *Qualifications for Success in Agriculture*   30
  IV. *Your Future in Agriculture*   37
   V. *Education for Careers in Agriculture*   40
  VI. *Women in Agriculture*   46
 VII. *The Agricultural Chemical Industry*   48
VIII. *Agricultural Education Including Agricultural Extension*   56
  IX. *Agricultural Engineering*   67
   X. *Agricultural Science and Research*   77
  XI. *Animal Industries*   85
 XII. *Business and Industry in Agriculture*   100
XIII. *Communications and Public Relations in Agriculture*   110
XIV. *Conservation of Natural Resources and Rural Recreation*   118
 XV. *Farming, Production, and Ranching*   123
XVI. *Food Technology and Processing*   134
XVII. *Government Careers for Agricultural Graduates*   142
XVIII. *Plant Sciences—Agronomy, Botany, Forestry, Horticulture*   154
XIX. *Rural Social Science*   171

     Appendix I. Educational Institutions Offering Instruction in Agriculture   174
     Appendix II. National Associations   184
     Appendix III. Correspondence Study   188
     Appendix IV. Bibliography   189

Preface

During the past dozen years of close association with college and high-school students, I have wished many times for a publication that presented a broad picture of the numerous career opportunities in the agricultural industry. The large number of outstanding rural and urban youths interested in science, business, and education need to be acquainted with the career possibilities in agriculture. The author has been stimulated by his contact with college students seeking employment and high-school students who were on the threshold of deciding between a college education and finding employment immediately following high school.

I am hopeful that the information in this book will arouse interest in the thousands of careers in agriculture that are open to young people with enthusiasm for a stimulating career.

I am grateful to my wife Virginia and my two daughters and their families for encouragement and assistance. I also appreciate the assistance and encouragement received from colleagues, former students, and friends.

Chester S. Hutchison

Introduction

This book was written for the young people who are interested in agriculture as a career. It is also intended for the parents, teachers, and counselors who have a sympathetic understanding of their children's career interests.

Agriculture is a science, a business, a profession, or an industry, depending upon the segment being considered. Are you one of the persons who still think of agriculture as farming, and of farming as tilling the soil and caring for livestock? Such concepts are out of date in our present era.

True commercial farming remains the backbone of the agricultural industry, since more money is spent for food products than any other category of basic goods or services. The farmer is an important businessman, scientist, and mechanic; he stands at the center of a vast network of industrial, commercial, management, and educational facilities that provide employment for a third of the working people in our nation.

Food products from the farm go through many steps before reaching the ultimate consumer. They must be assembled, financed, graded, processed, packaged, stored, and delivered. These services are best performed or supervised by persons with agricultural training.

The agricultural industry only begins with the farmer or producer; it also includes unlimited areas and services that appeal to an increasingly large number of young career seekers.

A rural background, while helpful, is not essential to a career in agriculture. Today young men and women who have lived in cities all their lives are seeking training in agricultural colleges in preparation for careers in one of the numerous phases of the agricultural industry.

This book is therefore organized to help Future Farmer advisers, Scout leaders, service club committees, 4-H Club leaders, and religious leaders in their discussions of careers with urban young people as well as rural youths who want to stay in agriculture but have to leave the farm.

YOUR FUTURE IN AGRICULTURE

Chapter I

Choosing a Career

A high-school student or graduate must make many important decisions. Two of the most important are the choice of his life work and the educational training necessary to prepare for it. Making these decisions wisely is essential for several reasons. The choice of a career may determine whether one has steady employment or is frequently unemployed. During economic depressions as many as 70 per cent of the persons in some career areas are unemployed while fewer than 10 per cent in other areas are out of work.

The choice of a career may determine success or failure, may determine whether one likes or dislikes his work, may influence his home and community living, and often determines the economic and social status of his family. Abilities, likes and dislikes, and personal needs are important considerations in the choice of a career. Opportunities for employment should be considered in light of one's aptitudes, interests, and limitations.

You have probably thought of three or four occupations which appeal to you as a lifetime career. You have been studying your interests and abilities. But how far have you traveled along the road toward selection of your career?

Answers to the following questions, carefully thought out and perhaps written down for future reference, should help you judge your fitness for each type of work that interests you. Your family, friends, counselors, and teachers can help you answer the questions. Sometimes you will find the information in work experience and in books which your counselors, teachers, and librarians can recommend.

1. Do you have the necessary abilities to do the work demanded in the career you are considering?
   a) What are the duties involved in the job?
   b) What skills are needed to perform the duties?
   c) What personal qualifications are required?

2. How do you prepare for the career of your interest?
   a) What type of training is needed?
   b) What special aptitudes must you possess?
   c) What degree of intelligence is needed?
   d) Can you afford the training necessary to prepare for the career?
   e) Where is the training available?
3. How will you enter the career?
   a) What job experiences will serve as preparation for the career of your choice?
   b) What part does chance play in your finding employment in one of the stepping-stone jobs?
4. What other careers are available that can use your abilities, qualifications, and training?
5. Is your training sufficiently broad to prepare you for other jobs in a career that would satisfy you?

Sound occupational information is essential to the selection of the career or careers that will meet your interests and abilities, and it may be obtained from many sources. Firsthand information can often be secured by visits to establishments in business, industry, science and research, food production, food processing and distribution, education, communication, conservation, and many other career areas. A field trip or individual visit to study specific jobs thoroughly will often reveal new information about careers. Other direct sources of career information include occupational and community surveys made by schools, government agencies, and community organizations.

Government Sources

Various government agencies regularly compile and publish occupational information that will be helpful in studying careers. This information is often available in the offices of high-school counselors, local libraries, and employment officers.

The "Dictionary of Occupational Titles and Codes" is available at the local employment office and often may be obtained in the school library. Colleges and trade schools provide counseling services and career information for young people who are considering additional training for specific careers.

Commercial Publications

Many industrial and business organizations have occupational information which they use for recruiting. Such booklets and leaflets can be secured through a high-school counselor, a local official of the company concerned, or by writing directly to the personnel department of the company. Local industries have business associations, personnel associations, foremen's clubs, etc., which may provide information and materials. In larger cities, the Chamber of Commerce may have a department that compiles and distributes occupational information.

College Placement Offices

Most colleges and universities have placement offices that work closely with industry, government agencies, agriculture, and the professions. The placement officer is acquainted with the opportunities available and the training needed to enter careers which require a college education. The college placement officers and employer representatives have joined forces to form regional placement associations in the United States and Canada to increase the effectiveness of placement to the employer as well as to the college graduate.

The "College Placement Annual," the official directory of the placement associations, includes basic data on more than 1,500 firms and agencies that regularly recruit on college campuses. The annual is available in most college placement offices.

Job Opportunities

Today's goods and services demand an increasing percentage of better educated and more highly trained workers. The basic trends in employment during recent years indicate that our growing economy will require more professional and technical people in the years ahead. There will be substantial increases in the number of managers, proprietors, sales people, craftsmen, and trained service workers, while the need for unskilled labor will decline.

The decline in the need for farmers and farm workers is offset by the increase in the size of farms and the need for persons trained in the management, production, and technology of today's more mechanized and more specialized farms and farm industries.

Through the years there has been a steady increase in the percentage of high-school graduates who go to college. College education has gained a higher rating as programs have been applied more directly to specific fields in the world's activities. Science is definitely influencing the tasks of men and women, and nowhere is it more important than in the field of agriculture.

It is true that one may engage in farming without going to college. The same is true of many other technical vocations. College education calls for the best that a man has; it calls for men with keen minds and a driving ambition. College education will not insure a person against failure, but it will help to develop the ability for greater earning power.

There are two kinds of jobs—those jobs open only to college graduates with a knowledge of science and technical training, and those open to men with or without a college education. A college education will improve the chances for success in any job and greatly increase the compensation in most areas.

College Training in Agriculture

"Agriculture" is a big word and means many things. It means land, animals, growing things, and homes. The problems facing the agriculturists of today and tomorrow are innumerable. The rural community is not made up of farmers alone. Each rural community must be served by teachers, local leaders, and many individuals in other professions, all interwoven into the clear understanding and appreciation of what agriculture means. Agriculture is a great profession, and any great industry needs men with the best of preparation and training.

Experience is a great teacher, but it is also an expensive teacher. Many difficulties can be avoided by a knowledge of the scientific principles involved in agricultural practices. Education for those who remain on the farm should involve more than the development of skills. The young men and women who enter agriculture or one of its allied fields should have a complete undertanding of the elements of farming as a science and as a business.

The products of the farm, in addition to being produced, must be assembled from the farms, financed, processed, graded, packaged, transported, stored, and delivered. These steps have given rise to a large number of services which in many cases are performed by persons with agricultural background and training.

Young people reared on farms should be aware of the need for more training to meet the growing specialization on our farms. The use of science, engineering, and good management practices has resulted in commercial farming that involves the use of capital, credit, chemicals, and specialized machinery.

Every year 15,000 new jobs are available for college graduates in agricultural fields. Opportunities exist in every area of agriculture for young men and women with college backgrounds. The following chapters of this book will explore opportunities in various phases of agriculture.

Research—Includes Production, Marketing, Economics, Processing, Agricultural Engineering, Equipment and Utilities, Utilization of By-Products, Rural Sociology, Conservation and Utilization of Natural Resources.

Industry—Includes Food Processing, Grain and Seed Processing, Machinery and Equipment, Meat and Meat Packing, Chemicals, Feed Manufacturing, Herbicides and Pesticides, Dairy Processing, Forestry, Textiles and Fibers, Buildings, Utilities, Public Relations.

Business—Includes Banking and Credit, Cooperative Management, Land Appraisal, Grading, Inspection, Packaging, Food Distribution, Marketing, Farm Utilities, Private Business.

Education—Includes Vocational Agriculture, Agricultural Extension, College Instruction, Government Agencies, Farm Organizations, International Technical Aid.

Communications—Includes Farm Reporting, Market Reporting, Publications, Magazines, Advertising, Public Relations, Radio and Television, Photography, and Motion Pictures.

Conservation—Includes Soil, Water, Range, Forest, Fish, and Wildlife Conservation; Parks and Turf Management.

Service—Includes Quality Control, Inspection, Grading, Regulation, Foreign Agricultural Service, Technical, Consulting, and Veterinary Services.

Farming and Ranching—Includes General Farming; Dairy, Swine, Beef, Sheep, Poultry, Cotton, Fruit, Nursery, Vegetable, Grain, and Seed Production; and other specialties.

Farm youths who can go to college should be aware of the opportunities in professional agricultural occupations. For those who do not attend college, the growing demand for craftsmen, operatives, and individuals for certain services can be met with training in vocational schools.

Of particular importance is an understanding of the dynamic nature of our economy. New methods of production and processing, new products, new services, and new patterns of living are continually causing changes in the kinds of jobs available. This process calls for a broad foundation of training and education to enable the graduate to make a smooth transition from one occupation or field of work to another if change becomes necessary.

Chapter II

The Character of Modern Agriculture

The citizens of the United States have the highest standard of living in the world. This has been made possible by our ability to produce food efficiently in larger quantities than the people can consume.

Today's agriculture is a highly complex, integrated, dynamic industry. A great change has taken place since the days when a farmer used a horse or two, grew his own feed and forage, saved his own seed, and produced vegetables and fruit for his own family and a little extra to purchase staples needed throughout the year.

Now the picture is quite different. The modern commercial farmer is much more dependent upon associated industries for maintaining his production and distribution.

Farming beyond question is a declining industry in terms of number of farms, number of workers, and percentage of the total national output. In the long run, this is a desirable adjustment from all viewpoints. Yet in any meaningful sense agriculture is far from being a declining industry. At present, some two-thirds of the value of American raw materials are represented by farm products, and about one-fifth of American export trade is based on agricultural products. Agricultural products are important as raw products for industry. Land, buildings, and equipment in farming represent about 10 per cent of American capital. Farmers, suppliers to farmers, and customers of farmers are major capital users. Between one-fifth and one-fourth of American disposable income is spent on foods and fibers. These are not declining industries. The changes that have occurred in them in the past twenty years are greater in scope and degree than those of the preceding two hundred years.

Agriculture's Success Story

Fewer than seven million farmers in the United States are able to give us the highest agricultural production in the world. Our nation stands first both in the size and diversity of its output and ranks

21

among the highest in the efficiency of its agriculture and the quality of its farm products.

The bargain that the American consumers get in food is unmatched anywhere in the world. We enjoy the lowest food costs and one of the world's richest and most nutritious diets. There has been a massive shift from the cheaper starchy foods to the more luxurious high-protein, high-vitamin foods—meat, milk, fruits, and vegetables. We spend only 20 per cent of our income on food today; and if we ate the cheaper foods that made up the diet twenty-five years ago, the cost would be only 16 per cent of the average family budget.

These are some of the less well-known successes of agriculture that need to be told again and again.

The farmer's share of the national income has steadily dwindled as he has helped to build the nation's agricultural output. In the past fifteen years, his share in the national income has dropped from 10 per cent to 4 per cent while personal income for the nation as a whole has more than doubled.

The improvement in the farm income situation includes such factors as record marketings of farm products, higher price supports for major crops, and new farm programs. Although production expenses have absorbed about a third of the gain, it appears that the net income of successful, efficient farm operators will improve in the future.

In colonial days, about 85 per cent of the population had to work the land to feed themselves and the remaining 15 per cent. Today less than 8 per cent are farming and feeding themselves and the other 92 per cent, with surpluses left over to feed the world's hungry wherever they may be.

Today, farmers function as just one part of a wholly new agriculture, often referred to as agribusiness. For every farmer on the land, three or four persons working in related lines of business are needed to keep him going.

The Nation's Biggest Industry

Farming employs seven million workers—more than are employed in the steel industry, the automobile industry, or transportation and public utilities combined, according to statistics collected by the U.S. Department of Agriculture.

Investment in agriculture exceeds $203,000,000,000, equal to 75 per cent of the value of current assets of all corporations in the United

States, or 75 per cent of the market value of all stocks on the New York Stock Exchange.

The investment in agriculture represents $29,000 for each farm employee, as compared with $15,900 for each worker in manufacturing industry.

Farmers are also good customers of other industries. They spend $25,000,000,000 to $26,000,000,000 a year for goods and services to produce crops and livestock; another $15,000,000,000 a year for the same things that city dwellers buy—food, clothing, drugs, furniture, appliances, and other products and services.

Four out of every ten jobs in private employment are related to agriculture—ten million people have jobs storing, transporting, processing, and merchandising farm products, and six million have jobs providing the supplies farmers use.

The 1960 census reported that 3 per cent of American farms, the 134,000 largest, did more than 30 per cent of total farm business. The 45 per cent largest American commercial farms did well over 90 per cent of the business. Thus, 55 per cent of the farms in the American economy did less than 10 per cent of the business. Actually, the 35 per cent smallest American farms did only 4 per cent of the value of farm sales. Upgrading of commercial activity has been concentrated in the smallest farms.

The Agribusiness Partners

As we have said, agriculture is much more than farming. Nonetheless, farming or production constitutes a very important part of our national economy. As of the 1960 census, there were approximately 3,700,000 farm operators in the United States; they gross more than $38,000,000,000 in annual sales. And yet, today's farmer would be virtually helpless without the supply and service industries that provide him with the inputs of agricultural production. In fact, without the agribusiness suppliers of agricultural goods and services, he would have difficulty producing enough food to feed his own family. In most instances he would have no source of power and would be able to produce only what he could manage with a hoe and a shovel. The off-farm supply and service agencies are thus as important to modern agriculture as is the farmer himself. Together they comprise a team—a team that might be called one pair of the five strong partners of the agribusiness team. The farm production supply and service industry in the

United States employs 5,600,000 people and has an annual payroll of over $24,000,000,000.

Just as our farmer of today is dependent on the off-farm supplies and services he purchases, so he would have difficulty in realizing a decent income from his agricultural products without the marketing and processing agencies. In the United States today there are 26,000 firms that take agricultural products from the farm and transform them into food for human consumption. These firms employ 3,000,-000 people and have a $14,000,000,000 annual payroll. They add $30,000,000,000 each year to the value of the produce they handle.

Still another segment of modern agriculture is the wholesaling of agricultural products—moving them through the channels of trade toward the consumer. This segment of agribusiness, comprising nearly 88,000 firms, employs over 1,000,000 people; its annual payroll amounts to $4,000,000,000, and its annual sales are in excess of $100,000,000,000.

Retail sales of agricultural products in the United States account for more than 3,000,000 employees, an $8,000,000,000 annual payroll, and over $81,000,000,000 in estimated annual sales. There are more than 800,000 retail establishments throughout the country.

In the aggregate, therefore, some 16,000,000 of our 66,796,000 employed workers are involved in modern agriculture. That is 24 per cent of the total labor force—a far different matter from the 10 per cent quoted when only farm workers are included in the definition of agriculture.

The nine out of ten farm youths who must seek their careers off the farm thus have a choice of pursuits undreamed of by yesterday's farm youngster. For some jobs, vocational agriculture courses may offer sufficient training, but others require advanced study in genetics, agronomy, chemistry, biology, geology, forestry, entomology, animal husbandry, zoology, veterinary medicine, farm management, agricultural engineering, food technology, processing, marketing, public relations, journalism, salesmanship—the list is almost endless.

Other Related Fields

It is difficult to think of any kind of competence which could not find some application in agriculture.

For instance, a banker who wants to build up a good loan business among farmers must employ men who know not only the business of financing but also the business of farming. How else could they properly appraise a farmer's assets and liabilities and his capacity for earning enough to repay a loan?

The manager of a supermarket must either know, or hire someone who knows, when and what to buy—and whether the price is right. He must have more than farm background to do this, of course, but farm background gives him a head start.

Chemists developing insecticides and pesticides not only must be proficient in their own field but also must know something about the crops they are trying to protect and the hazards they are combatting.

Government alone, at the Federal, state, and county level, accounts for a tremendous staff of agricultural workers. Recently it was reported that an inspection corps of 1,900 workers was employed solely in checking processed poultry going across state lines in normal channels of trade.

But enticing as some of the off-the-farm jobs may be, migration will not be entirely away from farms. Occasionally a city man will break out of the pattern and move into farming—not, as once might have been the case, because he could not make a go of anything else, but because farming is what he most wants to do.

Despite promising opportunities, in agriculture as in industry, unemployment and underemployment exist right beside unfilled jobs because of a scarcity of qualified applicants. It has been estimated that as many as 20,000 new jobs in agriculture-related work become available annually, with no more than 8,000 applicants able to qualify.

Yet some of these new types of farm-related jobs offer as much excitement as can be found anywhere.

Agricultural workers may, in fact, prove to be no more earthbound in their endeavors than the astronauts themselves. As men move nearer to ultimate mastery over outer space and establish outposts on the moon and elsewhere, wholly new forms of nutrition will be needed for the human beings undertaking planetary adventures.

Since 70 per cent of today's crop varieties in the United States were unknown as recently as twenty years ago, there can be little doubt that whatever is needed will be developed and that those engaged in such development will be a new kind of pioneers. Already, research is evolving the necessary form and packaging of food for men in space, and, like most interplanetary research, this effort is still in its infancy.

The needs of space explorers and colonists may even dictate development of wholly new kinds of crops right here on earth—just as the necessity for perfecting machine harvesters has led to the modification of certain crop varieties to make the plants conform to the requirements of machine handling. The types of food that may be developed for cultivation on other planets belong, so far, to the science-fiction category, but one thing is certain: These advances can come no faster than men are prepared to push them.

Looking Toward the Future

In general, success in farm-related careers in the future will belong more than ever to the man or woman who is especially prepared to serve an exceedingly complex and competitive business.

Except for the relatively few grains and fibers in which maladjustment problems are localized, American farmers have made remarkable adaptation to the changes in demands of American consumers. Demands for fruit and vegetable products, dairy products, eggs, and —to a lesser extent—meats and poultry have risen. These have been paralleled by long-run declines in the level of demand for cereals, potatoes, and similar products. Perhaps more important, the size of processing and distribution firms has grown immensely, and the relationships among firms at different functional levels have become closer.

Population is now growing at the rate of about 1.6 per cent annually. Other things being equal, a 1 per cent increase in population means a 1 per cent increase in food demand. As times goes on, the effect of economic growth and of increasing per capita purchasing power, already small, will diminish. The weighted per capita index of food consumption has risen about 10 per cent over the past twenty years. There may be a 5 per cent to 10 per cent increase in per capita food consumption over the next decade, but probably no such increase will occur in response to higher incomes after 1980; by that time most people will be able to afford to eat as they wish, and further increases in income will not be spent on food. There is already considerable leveling off in the per capita consumption of certain foods.

By 1975, the market for foods and fibers may be 40 per cent larger than that of 1955-1957. Population may have increased by as much as one-third, and a 10 per cent increase could conceivably emerge from changes in the size and distribution of real income. Preference patterns among foods will probably reflect present trends. A 1975 population ranging from 210,000,000 to 225,000,000 will show the largest relative increases in the Pacific and Southern areas. Food demands will be affected by concentration in low and high age groups within the population as well as by a continued shift toward the suburbs. Consequently, present trends toward light, convenience, and prefabricated food items can be expected to continue well through the decade of the 1960s. By 1975, there may be as many as 90,000,000 people in the labor force, with sharp changes in age and sex distributions. If the nation remains at peace, there should be a long-run decrease in the workweek and an annual unemployment level of not over 4 to 5 per cent of the labor force. Conservatively, per capita income may be expected to rise at an annual average rate of from 2 to 2½ per cent, reflecting greater capitalization and consequent productivity. Over all, the annual average increase in the real value of goods and services should range from 3 to 3½ per cent. Expenditures on consumption goods may be as much as 60 per cent higher than in 1955-1957, assuming a near-doubling of the gross national product and no increase in the relative part thereof devoted to government expenditure.

About one-fifth of the capital assets of this nation are used in farming. There is an investment of $29,000 per wage earner, or twice the average per capita capitalization in other industries. The importance of capital and credit in the past twenty years has been associated with the substitution of machinery and equipment for labor, a trend which will continue. It is expected that by 1975 there will be a lower percentage rate of increase in the value of productive assets per worker. Perhaps there will be a higher rate of increase in the use of short-term capital for fertilizer, feed, chemicals, and similar inputs.

The food and agricultural industries are becoming commercialized at all levels. Relationships among food processors, distributors, and producers must almost inevitably grow closer. The drastic changes in relative size of enterprise; in the use of power and equipment as substitute for labor; in markets, marketing methods, and channels; and in the nature of farm products themselves must almost inevitably continue along present lines. Aside from commodity and regional adjustments, farmers everywhere must make continued adjustment in the product itself; in their own internal methods of meeting the requirements of customers and the facilities of suppliers; and in the making of the markets. This is not a dying industry. By 1975 it will represent no more than 4 per cent of the gross national product, but it will still be a bigger and better customer for credit than it is now.

Thus, the basic question involves looking to the future with respect to the production, procurement, and merchandising activities of agricultural enterprises; changes in product, factor, and markets; and changes in government programs. The direct interest of bankers in agricultural enterprises as credit customers is fortified by the fact that firms serving as suppliers to agriculture and the processors and distributors, who are the customers of agriculture, are also huge industries with large credit needs closely interlocked with the farms of the nation.

Finally, the distribution agencies, sales forces, markets, and supermarkets come into place to move the product into the homemaker's kitchen where meals may be prepared at a minimum of cost and effort.

Thus, it becomes apparent that the agricultural enterprise, whether it be dairying or production of field, fruit, or vegetable crops, poultry, or greenhouse and nursery crops, is a highly integrated system. The farmers are a basic essential but, as pointed out, in a minority. The number of American farm units has dropped almost 50 per cent in twenty-seven years, from 6,500,000 to 3,500,000. In New York State there are 80,000 farms. Yet, in 1959, New York farmers spent $100,-000,000 for equipment repairs and parts, $178,000,000 for feedstuffs, and $36,000,000 for fertilizers. They sold almost $1,000,000,000 worth of produce. It may seem an exaggeration to claim that 25 per cent of New York business is in agriculture, yet, in addition to the farms, there are 2,500 firms providing supplies and 70,000 businesses assembling, processing, and distributing farm products. This means a total of 500,000 persons employed in agriculture, a truly significant group.

We have achieved a food-supply situation in the United States that is the envy of countries throughout the world. This has been done without adding to cost at a rate comparable to the cost-of-living index. Today, 20 per cent of our disposable income will buy a better diet than 25 per cent of our income would buy in 1940.

Agriculture is expected to provide the consumer with food of good quality. In fact, the general public demands a perfect product. It must be attractive to look at, have good flavor and texture, and be highly nutritious. Above all, it must be free from harmful chemical residues.

The key to the present prosperity of agriculture and its future success is research. Research has formed the basis for the tremendous revolution in methodology in farming. Looking ahead to the problems of competition for world markets or even between states, we can see a real challenge. The rapid expansion of world population and its accompanying need for more foodstuffs should give us concern, for we will need knowledge that we do not have at this time.

Chapter III

Qualifications for Success in Agriculture

A rural background, while helpful, is not essential to a career in agriculture. Alert young men and women who have lived all their lives in cities have been trained for employment in agriculture and have been highly successful.

The factors that contribute to the success of an agricultural business are the knowledge, initiative, efficiency, and ingenuity of the persons involved in it.

The agricultural industry begins with the farmer or producer, but it also includes unlimited areas and services that appeal to an increasingly large number of young men and women seeking careers. Food products must be produced by the farmer, assembled from the farms, processed, transported, stored, and delivered to the supermarkets and retail stores. These services, in many instances, are being performed by persons with agricultural background, training, and experience.

Packing plants, creameries, processing plants, and transportation companies, as well as wholesale and retail distribution agencies, are constantly looking for well-trained personnel. The many firms furnishing farmers with supplies and equipment also seek men familiar with the problems of agriculture.

These many activities require trained men to operate, manage, supervise, teach, inspect, merchandise, carry on research, handle public relations, conduct extension work, and engage in various other types of occupations. It is for these fields or services that the agricultural colleges are training men and women.

Farming still constitutes the chief employment of those engaged in agriculture. In farming, a great variety of talents can be utilized, from routine physical labor to highly trained persons in plant and animal breeding, disease and insect control, scientific feeding, and management of business units that involve many thousands of dollars.

If pursued intelligently, a career in farming offers a secure, stable lifetime of varied experiences and furnishes the three esssentials of a successful life: the necessary materials and services for comfortable, healthful living; a means of self-expression; and an avenue of service to others. Few occupations equal farming as a means of providing food, shelter, and a satisfying family life. Many organizations today want men only in the middle years of life, whereas farming can furnish satisfying employment for the whole life, from childhood to retirement.

In the early history of agriculture, when land was plentiful and the soil fertile, a man without special training had a fair chance of making a living as a producer of agricultural commodities. Conditions have changed. Such factors as soil fertility, plant and animal diseases, parasites, competition, location, transportation, marketing, and other controllable factors play important roles in present-day commercial farming.

The successful farmer today is a good businessman who has the knowledge and ability to increase his income by applying new ideas from many sources. He must know about the life of plants and the functions of their parts, about soil and its relation to plant growth, about insects, disease, bacteria, and fungi. His mind must remain open to new ideas. No longer is farming a matter of mere hard labor; it is a business to which one must bring a fund of information and practical experience as well as the will to work.

A trained farmer ranks with the doctor, merchant, engineer, scientist, and architect. He is all of these, wrapped up in one individual. He buys and sells, applies science in the selection of seeds, and fights pests. A well-trained farmer is interested in the latest practices of livestock management and crop production. He operates a variety of power-driven equipment, constructs buildings, and repairs machinery.

Even with the growing specialization in agriculture, the average farmer is probably called upon in the performance of his duties to have a wider variety of information at his command than any other businessman. A farmer cannot learn these things merely by casual observation.

Today's farmer uses the soil as the basis of all his enterprises. He must understand the science of crop production and soil management. The demands of a changing world call for flexibility in the cropping programs of our farms. A student of farming must become an expert in the principles of crop breeding and crop management. He must be familiar with the composition and properties of soil, the use of fertilizers, and the principles of soil conservation and proper land use.

The farm machinery of the early 1900s was relatively simple. Currently, the use of combines, tractors, and other power machinery demands mechanical skill and knowledge. In the same way, the early marketing of farm products was a simple matter. Now, without wise choice of crops, efficiency of production, and cooperative marketing, it may develop that the more the farmer raises, the less net profit he makes. In short, farming in the 1960s demands a wide range of information if the farmer expects to remain in the channels of competition.

Farming is peculiar in one respect; it combines business with home in an intimate manner scarcely true of any other occupation. Farm life appeals to many because the farmer is "his own boss." Aside from the general conditions and limitations of taxes, labor problems, transportation, debt, and the hundred and one other circumstances imposed by our broader economic life, the fact remains that the farmer plans his own day, works in his own way, and stops work at his own will. He has no clock to punch, no supervisor to please, none of the jealousies, bickerings, or politics of the shop or office to endure. His occupation has about it a certain independence which has tended to make the farmer a strong individualistic figure.

The day of isolation is past. Good roads and automobiles make it possible for the rural dweller to go to town for shopping trips, church, social activities, or entertainment almost as easily as the urbanite.

Research

Much of the research in agriculture-related industries such as fertilizer and feed companies, farm implement manufacturers, packing plants, and other food-processing plants is done by agriculturally trained persons. Recent advances in experimental work on food technology and nutrition open a new field of science for college graduates.

The perfect type of vocation or occupation or career is the one in which the young man or woman has the maximum interest and ability and the greatest promise of an opportunity for advancement.

When considering research in a branch of agriculture as a life work, young people should first study the opportunities; second, they should measure their interests by one or more of the tests available; and third, they should know the aptitudes necessary for a fair degree of success. In considering a type of agricultural research that calls for college training, the young person should investigate the facilities offered by the agricultural colleges. Each state has at least one such college that offers training in agriculture with a broad foundation of courses in sciences and the humanities.

Agricultural Selling

Selling has changed from a haphazard job to a trained career. Let us analyze the factors that contribute to successful selling. There are thousands of farm communities across America raising better crops and livestock, saving time and work, and having more comforts and conveniences due to successful salesmen.

Salesmanship is a dynamic power in agriculture. Many products used on the farm and in related businesses are manufactured hundreds of miles away. The distribution of labor-saving devices, supplies, and equipment needed to increase agricultural efficiency is the responsibility of agricultural salesmen.

A feed salesman in southern Indiana once remarked that "Successful salesmanship is helping someone decide on equipment, supplies, or service he'll be glad he bought."

A successful salesman is working as a counselor, or in an advisory capacity, building customer satisfaction. To be successful h∹ must have a knowledge of his product or service and know its advantage to the purchaser. He must have courage, since there will be many obstacles to overcome. He must recognize that there are achievements in the form of income, honors, and goals. Lastly, a successful salesman approaches his prospects, dealers and customers with a wholesome attitude.

The Basic Requirements of the Agriculturist

To achieve the goals of effective living in agriculture a young man needs the following qualifications:

1. The technical knowledge necessary to make decisions.
2. The managerial competence to organize and operate a business.
3. The basic tools for communication of ideas.

4. The ability to think critically about the social consequences of our material discoveries, the development of the earth, and the rational use of natural resources.
5. An acquaintance with history, politics, economics, and social problems in order to understand the forces that shape society into what it is today and will be tomorrow.
6. Some knowledge of the arts, philosophy, literature, and religion —for his enjoyment, for creative pursuits, and for a realization of the values that men have sought and should seek as individuals.

By this time you are probably wondering where to find persons who can meet these qualifications. Several years ago a leading magazine made a study, "What Does College Do for You?"

Until 1948 there had been no statistical picture of the nation's 4,966,000 college graduates. In that year research workers polled a representative cross section—those whose names began with the letters *Fa*—of all living college graduates. Of these, 9,064 returned ballots with answers to 134 questions. Alphabetically, the sample ranged from Oliver Wendell Faaborg of Willmar, Minn., a University of Minnesota graduate ('35), to Marie T. Fazzone of Bridgeport, Conn., fresh out of Connecticut College for Women ('47). The oldest was 91, the youngest 19.

For six months, banks of IBM machines sorted out the answers. The completed study included these conclusions:

Success. The U.S. college graduate is 49 times as likely as the noncollege man to be listed in "Who's Who in America" and nearly 15 times as likely to make $10,000 a year.

As far as his present income goes, it does not matter much what grades he earned at college: The "A" man averages only $49 a year more than his less scholarly fellow. It was observed that "A" students are more apt to enter lower-paid occupations such as teaching, science, and government service.

The college graduate is probably a professional man or a business executive. Only 1 per cent were farmers.

Attitudes. Only 26.3 per cent of the college graduates consider themselves Democrats, 38.3 per cent Republicans, the rest independents. The college graduate is much more likely to vote in national elections (78.9 per cent) than his noncollege neighbor.

The average graduate thinks that the differences between Russia and the U.S. can be reconciled without war and is anxious to see the United Nations strengthened. And he feels that all Americans— "Negroes, Jew , for ign-born, and others"—deserve an even break (80 per cent voted "yes").

Was College Worthwhile? Seven out of ten graduates believe their college courses helped them "a lot" in their present occupation. If they had it to do over again, 83.5 per cent would attend the same college, and only 2.1 per cent would not go to college at all. But one in four wishes he had chosen another major field, and those who would do it differently vote three-to-two for more specific vocational training.

Individual Maturity

A mature individual is one who can control his feelings, frustrations, and hostilities as he considers problems and makes decisions. He will approach each problem with facts and use all available infor ation as a guide to finding a solution.

Each mature person should be able to evaluate himself objectively and realistically and to recognize personal weaknesses and shortcomings without frustration. Mature persons respect the strengths, weaknesses, and abilities of other people and avoid the temptation to take advantage of others.

A man who is mature possesses a great degree of confidence in his own ability. He also gains great satisfaction from the accomplishments of others. He is patient, possesses strong principles, and has a sense of proportion.

Leadership

Leadership is recognized as the ability of a person to "go ahead and show the way." A leader is one who will show initiative when most people are apathetic; endure misunderstanding instead of seeking honor and glory; take a courageous stand when others are succumbing to expediency and timidity; plunge ahead when it is easy to drift with the tide; live up to parental, religious, home, and social obligations when there is a strong temptation to neglect or evade them; be a doer, not a complainer; and be alert to opportunities that will raise the standards of family life.

American agriculture needs executives, managers, and potential leaders for tomorrow. There is a shortage of men who know how to lead or who are willing to start at the bottom and move up the ladder to positions of responsibility.

Chapter IV

Your Future in Agriculture

We are living in an era of abundant food for the people of our nation, low farm income, increasing wages for nonfarm workers, improved highways, excellent communications, and a decrease in the number of farm businesses with an increase in the size of farm operations.

This might seem a situation holding little future for the young man interested in agriculture; but let us consider for a moment the many careers already outlined in this book and the fine educational opportunities for young men interested in the broad field of agriculture.

Agriculture is an industry with a capital investment of $200,000,-000,000. Some 7,000,000 people work on farms, 6,000,000 in processing, 10,000,000 in marketing, and from 250,000 to 500,000 in private and governmental research.

People will continue to eat and to spend approximately 20 per cent of their income for food. The food industry prospers because the consumer wants a large amount of high-quality, wholesome, nutritious food in convenient, time-saving packages.

Since 1940 we have witnessed an explosion of agricultural science and technology. The production capacity of commercial farms has increased 50 per cent, while there has been a decline of 35 per cent in farm employment. As a result of new knowledge, 45 per cent of our farmers produce about 90 per cent of the total commerical output.

The increase in the size of farms and in specialization has in many cases required large amounts of capital as human and animal power has been replaced by mechanical power. An investment of $100,000 or more per worker in land, buildings, machinery, and equipment is not uncommon in the agricultural areas of the nation.

The next decade will see an ever-mounting number of young people graduating from our colleges, accepting careers of responsibility in research, science, education, engineering, quality control, management, marketing, sales, production, and services in the following businesses* and industries:

Banking and Credit	Grading, Packaging, and Distri-
Building	bution
Chemical Products	Insurance
Cooperatives	Land Appraisal
Custom Services	Machinery and Equipment
Dairy Processing Plants	Marketing
Electric Power Companies	Meat and Poultry Packing
Farm Management	Pesticides and Herbicides
Farm Utilities	Pharmaceuticals
Fertilizer and Lime	Private Businesses
Food Processing	Real Estate
Forest Products	Seed and Grain Processing
Fuel Supply	

We are living in a world of change, with material things and economic, social, and even spiritual values being discarded, recreated, molded, and reshaped. Thus, we are faced with several cardinal principles that must be kept in mind as we prepare ourselves for the future.

Science and technology have revolutionized our industry, our agriculture, our homes, and our way of life. Man directs power rather than supplying it himself. Farm families, like their urban counterparts, will have more time for self-improvement, community activities, leisure, and recreation.

The population of the world is increasing at the rate of 24,000,000 a year. With world trade and international programs, many new careers will be created to meet the problems of producing and transporting food.

The successful producer of tomorrow will no longer be a "jack of all trades." He will be a specialist in one or more of three areas of farming—growing crops, managing livestock, and marketing products.

People are interested in intellectual, emotional, and spiritual needs

* An industry produces commodities, especially in manufacturing and processing, on so large a scale that problems of labor and capital are involved in a distinct branch of the trade; business is often an inclusive term, specifically naming the combined activities of those engaged in the pursuit or sale of commodities in related financial transactions.

as well as material needs. Our success will not depend solely on how well we keep up with our neighbors; on the number of automobiles, tractors, or acres we own or gadgets we have in our home, business, or factory; but on how well we have met the needs of our people at home and abroad.

Your future in agriculture will depend upon how well you have prepared for a lifetime career. Honest answers to the following questions should help you judge your fitness for the career you select.

A. Do you have the necessary qualifications and abilities to do the work?
   1. What duties are involved?
   2. What skills are necessary?
   3. What personal qualifications do you need?
B. Are you interested in the type of work and responsibilities of the work?
C. How do you prepare for this occupation?
   1. What type of training is needed?
   2. Can you afford this training?
   3. Is the training available?
D. How will you enter the occupation?
   1. Are you willing to start at the bottom?
E. Are there other satisfactory occupations that would use your qualifications and training?

Chapter V

Education for Careers in Agriculture

Employment in the United States has risen to record levels during recent years. More than 71,000,000 persons were gainfully occupied in the mid-1960s. At the same time, unemployment has been high; a conservative estimate placed the jobless at an average of 4,000,000, or between 5 and 6 per cent of the nation's total labor force.

Each year 3,000,000 new jobs must be created just to keep unemployment from rising. By 1975 the total labor force is expected to approximate 93,000,000. These estimates allow for an increase in unemployment to a potential 10 or 11 per cent.

Of the 71,000,000 employed in the nation, one of every three persons works in some area of agriculture. Agriculture supplies our food, most of our fiber, and some of our building materials. You can actually count more than a thousand occupations within the following eight major fields of agriculture.

1. *Agricultural Research*
   - Production
   - Marketing
   - Economics
   - Agricultural Engineering
   - Equipment and Utilities
   - Processing
   - New Products
   - By-Products
   - Conservation
   - Land Utilization
   - Rural Sociology
2. *Agricultural Industry*
   - Food Processing
   - Grain and Seed Processing

Meat and Poultry Packing
Fertilizer and Lime
Pesticides and Herbicides
Feed Manufacturing
Machinery and Equipment
Dairy Processing
Buildings and Utilities
Forest Products
Textiles and Fibers
Fats and Oils
3. *Agricultural Business*
   - Banking and Credit
   - Insurance
   - Farm Management
   - Cooperative Management

Land Appraisal and Selling
Grading, Packaging, and
  Labeling
Marketing
Storage and Warehousing
Transportation
Farm Utilities
Private Businesses

4. *Agricultural Education*
  Vocational Agriculture
  Agricultural Extension
  College Instruction
  Governmental Agencies
  Farm Organizations
  Industrial Agencies
  Business Firms
  International Technical Aid

5. *Agricultural Communications*
  Newspapers
  Farm Reporting
  Market Reporting
  Magazines
  Publications
  Photography
  Radio
  Television
  Advertising
  Exhibiting
  Motion Pictures

6. *Agricultural Conservation*
  Soil
  Water
  Wildlife
  Parks
  Recreation Centers
  Forest

Fish
Turf

7. *Agricultural Sciences*
  Veterinary Medicine
  Inspection and Regulation
    Food and Feed
    Seed and Fertilizer
    Chemicals
    Plant Quarantine
    Animal Quarantine
  Quality Control
  Organizations
  Foundations
  Technical
  Consulting
  Statistical
  Foreign Agricultural
    Service

8. *Production and Ranching*
  General
  Grain
  Livestock
  Dairy
  Swine
  Beef
  Sheep
  Poultry
  Cotton
  Forage
  Fruits
  Vegetables
  Tobacco
  Seeds
  Nursery
  Specialty

Recent surveys indicate that 18,000 to 20,000 new agricultural college graduates could find jobs each year in these major fields. At present, there is an average of between two and three jobs for each agricultural graduate. Thus, an agricultural graduate of a well-rounded training program, including humanities, social sciences, and natural sciences in addition to technical courses, may have his choice of numerous jobs.

College Programs

The land grant made by the United States under an act approved by President Abraham Lincoln on July 2, 1862, provided that each state be granted an amount of public land equal to 30,000 acres for each Senator and Representative to which the state was entitled by the apportionment of the Census of 1860.

The proceeds from the sale of these lands were to provide a source of funds to be used for the support and maintenance of at least one "college in each state where the learning shall be, without excluding other scientific and classical studies and including military tactics, to teach such branches of learning as are related to Agriculture and the Mechanical Arts in such manner as the legislature of the state may respectively prescribe in order to promote the liberal and practical education of the industrial classes in the several pursuits and professions of life."

In pioneer days agriculture meant production of crops, livestock, or food and fiber. In our present space age, agriculture includes a dynamic progress in production with research and education in agriculture and its related industries, businesses, and services.

The increased emphasis on research to improve processing, marketing, and utilization of agricultural commodities requires college-trained workers.

The U.S. Census data for 1958 show that education is a sound investment for young people who are interested in dollars. The investment in a college education resulted in annual income three times as great as that of a person with only a grade-school education and one and two-thirds higher than that of a high-school graduate.

The average annual income of college graduates in 1958 was $9,206, while the average high-school graduate received $5,567, and the person with only an elementary education received $3,096.

Agricultural workers of the future need well-rounded training to meet the accelerated tempo of our modern agriculture, which also demands specialization in its producers, scientists, businessmen, and educators.

The young men and women who have specialized are best equipped to take their rightful place in our modern agriculture.

Special and Vocational Education

Vocational agriculture is an educational program in the public schools to help those who are planning to work in production or farming and for those who would like to prepare for careers in agricultural areas closely related to farming.

Vocational agriculture includes basic educational training in animal, plant, and soil science; agricultural mechanics; farm management and agricultural business; and agricultural leadership. This training is accomplished through organized instruction in the classroom and related occupational experience, both programs under the direction of competent teachers who have completed a specially designed four-year agricultural college program.

Vocational agriculture programs are designed to train high-school students who wish to explore opportunities for careers in: (1) agricultural production; (2) agricultural business; and (3) the agricultural professions.

The programs also offer training for adults who are employed and wish to improve their knowledge, earning power, and opportunities for advancement. This training is for persons interested in: (1) farming; (2) agricultural business; (3) professional careers in agriculture; (4) areas in occupations requiring knowledge of agriculture; and (5) agricultural production or service occupations.

Vocational Agriculture Programs

The rapid changes in modern agriculture have resulted in vocational agriculture programs to include four general areas of agricultural employment opportunities.

1. *On-the-farm occupations.* This instruction and training is designed for farm operators, managers, and other individuals who are employed in farming, including crop and livestock production.

2. *Special areas of agricultural production.* This instruction and special training consists of horticultural production including fruit and vegetable production, nursery stock and floriculture production,

landscape and greenhouse work. The employment opportunities in these special areas include operators, managers, and skilled and semiskilled workers.

3. *Nonproduction agricultural occupations.* The training and experience programs in this area are for individuals who are or will be employed in agricultural businesses, industries, and service organizations. Career opportunities exist in farm elevators; feed, fertilizer, and supply stores; farm machinery and equipment stores; garden and supply centers; food processing and others.

4. *Technical training in agribusiness.* The program is designed for individuals desiring to become agribusiness technicians in: (1) feed and farm supply services; (2) marketing farm produce, grain, and livestock; (3) selection, use, and application of farm chemicals and fertilizers; and (4) seed selection and use.

These programs usually require 20 to 30 class hours per week, 36 weeks each year for two years. The class work is integrated with a training period of practical experience.

Licensed Occupations

The occupations in agriculture that require a license are relatively few as compared with other fields. A person interested in a career in the following occupations should contact the state department of agriculture or other agency responsible for state, local, or Federal licensing in his state.

1. Auctioneer
2. Beekeeping
3. Commercial fishing
4. Commercial pheasant preserve operator
5. Dairy plant processing
6. Frozen-food locker management
7. Inspection and grading of dairy products, fruits and vegetables, and poultry and poultry products
8. Manufacturing of agricultural liming materials, fertilizers, and livestock feeds and remedies
9. Milk weigher, sampler, and tester
10. Nursery (plant materials) dealer
11. Seed agent or dealer

12. Seed and soil inoculant manufacturing
13. Wholesale produce dealer

Summary

Young people considering careers in agriculture should contact their local high-school counselor, teacher of vocational agriculture, county extension agent, employment counseling section of the state employment service, or a friend to explore the training experience and education needed to enter the occupation in which they are interested.

Chapter VI

Women in Agriculture

Women are playing an important role in the economy of our country by preparing for careers in business, the professions, and government. To compete successfully, women must plan for careers by demonstrating academic excellence in high school and college as well as acquiring work experience while in school to demonstrate their ability.

Today, eight in every ten employed women with a college degree are in professional, technical, or managerial jobs. These three areas are generally considered at the top of the career ladder. Even though women appear to have reached the top, there is evidence that college women generally have not reached the top positions, which are usually filled by men.

The outlook for women in many areas related to agriculture is not as bright as many believe. How college women actually fit into the future employment in agriculture will depend on their career planning, the attitude of employers, and the competition for available jobs.

The employment profile and advancement patterns in civilian Federal employment indicate that 47 per cent of the women had resigned at the end of two and a half years, as compared with 6 per cent of the men. Almost half of the women who leave Federal agencies give reasons related to family responsibilities. A few leave for better pay and to gain broader experience.

Employment trends suggest that a college education is necessary for a woman. Counselors, parents, and women need to develop a greater awareness of the importance of career planning in light of the kind of competition confronting women seeking employment in years ahead.

The tendency in the past has been to take a "job" rather than plan for a "career." The present necessity for college women to select a curriculum usually requires some college orientation and planning. The employment of women increases in proportion to the amount of education obtained.

Employed women as a proportion of all women 18 years and over in the United States, by level of education, in three specific years ranked as follows:

Level of Education	Per Cent Employed		
	1952	*1957*	*1962*
Elementary School			
Less than 8 years	27	25	23
8 years	30	30	28
High School			
Less than 4 years	34	34	34
4 years	40	40	41
College			
Less than 4 years	37	41	41
4 years or more	50	55	57

The percentage of all women with a college degree who were employed climbed from 50 per cent to 57 per cent in the ten-year period, while women with less than four years of high school remained the same or declined during the same period.

Women with degrees in agriculture have found careers in such fields of specialization as biochemistry, animal science, agricultural research, food technology, rural sociology, cooperative extension work, biology, botany, plant pathology, floriculture, ornamental horticulture, zoology, and entomology, to mention only a few.

Women are teaching; conducting research, technical assistance services, and investigations; writing; and performing other services in public relations, quality control, sales, and management in some businesses.

Chapter VII

The Agricultural Chemical Industry

The agricultural chemical industry will be a billion-dollar industry by 1970 or earlier. This prediction is made on the basis of its expansion during the past two decades; it has grown from $39,000,000 in 1940 to $500,000,000 in 1963.

The industry comprises about 300 companies that manufacture and distribute basic pesticide chemicals. Some of these companies and other members of the industry formulate the basic chemicals into finished products for use by the farmer, the home owner, industry, and government agencies in the control of insects, plant diseases, weeds, and rodents.

Does the growth of this agricultural specialty sound like a declining industry? The answer is definitely no, since more chemicals will be needed to improve farming efficiency if we are to meet the growing food needs of this nation and the world. As new uses are discovered for chemicals and new chemicals are developed, we will see greater use of them in farming, home gardening, parks, roadside maintenance, lawn management, forest pest control, and public health protection.

If you are inquisitive about the world we live in and enthusiastic about laboratory work, then agricultural chemistry may be your field.

The modern chemist in agriculture is improving the quality of food by testing raw materials, preventing losses in processing and storage, and devising better handling methods; turning waste products into usable goods in the field of chemurgy; discovering how to prevent loss of our natural goods by controlling insects and diseases; preventing fraud and injury by examining foods and other goods on our markets; and learning how improved farming practices can result in better products.

Through research on insecticides and fungicides enormous crops of orchard, garden, and animal products are saved each year from insects, parasites, and blights. Chemurgists learn to utilize the culls, trimmings, hulls, and by-products of manufacturing by converting such wastes to textiles, paper, plastics, motor fuels, paints, and endless other valuable commodities. Food technologists in chemistry work with industrial food companies, testing raw materials, controlling manufacturing processes, and otherwise insuring uniformly high-grade products.

The food and nutritional chemist may study composition of foods, their digestibility, biological value, distribution, and storage in the body; chemical reactions within the body; waste materials produced; and formulation of diets that meet requirements of healthy, productive animals.

There is a special field for the chemist who wants to work with dairy products. He conducts research on the composition, chemical and nutritional changes during processing, packaging, and storing of dairy products. He may work with milk, butter, cheese, ice cream, and all other foods connected with dairy work.

Changes in our living conditions and communities have created certain problems that can be solved only by persons with a knowledge of chemistry. The loss of agricultural production through the ravages of insects, diseases, and weeds is being stemmed by young men and women who have been trained in the chemistry of plants, insecticides, fungicides, and weed control. The chemical industries require control in manufacture and research for the discovery of more effective products at a cheaper price.

Employment Opportunities

The Federal government has established four regional laboratories carrying on research to find new uses for agricultural products. Many municipal, state, and Federal laboratories are maintained to insure proper labeling and standard quality of products according to law. The state agricultural experiment stations and the United States Department of Agriculture maintain research laboratories where problems in various fields of agricultural chemistry are being investigated.

The trained agricultural biochemist may find a place on the faculty of a state agricultural college. He may teach in his major field and cooperate with other departments such as animal science, poultry science, dairy science, botany, and home economics.

The opportunities for the biochemist are ever growing broader.

From the government laboratories to the large private food and textile producers and from the state universities to private research foundations, the need for the practical scientist is becoming ever more pressing. In some fields, as the dairy industry, the demand far exceeds the supply of competent, trained men.

The chemist who is interested in the plant world has a broad field for research. As a phytochemist he is concerned with such problems as the composition of plants, chemical processes taking place in plant tissue, storage of constituents, function of minerals, conditions affecting color of fruit and vegetables, action of chlorophyll in photosynthesis, study of plant hormones, and others.

College graduates are developing new uses for agricultural products. The agricultural biochemist is playing an important role in creating chemical changes that are concerned with production, processing, and utilization of foods and agricultural products.

The young man and woman who enjoys working in the sciences will find many challenging problems in working with the chemistry of foods, their utilization, and the physical and chemical changes that take place in animal and plant production. They may assist in discovering new products and new uses for old materials. Hundreds of chemists are needed to test raw materials, to control manufacturing processes, and to insure quality products.

Industrial Opportunities

The *food industries* of the United States do an annual business approaching $10,000,000,000. Hundreds of chemists are needed to test raw materials, to control manufacturing processes, and to insure uniformly high-grade products. Many other chemists are engaged in research to discover better methods of processing, to prevent deterioration of quality in raw materials and processed products, and to invent new food products that will better meet the needs of the consumer in convenience, palatability, and nutritional values. The utilization of culls, trimmings, hulls, and waste or by-products provides many problems for research.

The *insecticide and fungicide industry* requires chemical control in manufacture and research for the discovery of cheaper, more effective, and safer products. Enormous losses of field, orchard, and garden crops and of animal products result from uncontrolled attack of various bugs, blights, and parasites. The control and research chemist is an important part of the organization of any insecticide and fungicide factory.

The *fermentation industries* require chemists to control and improve the quality of the various beverages, solvents, acids, alcohols, and other products that are produced through the action of microorganisms or enzymes from starch or starchy products.

The *manufacturers of livestock feeds* require agricultural chemists in order to insure uniform composition of their products and to supply feeds that will properly meet the nutritional needs of the livestock to be fed. All large-scale manufacturers maintain both control and research laboratories.

Other industries employ agricultural chemists for many purposes. For example, the soybean processors extract oil, protein, and various other products from soybeans. These products are used in foods, paints, plastics, artificial wool fibers, adhesives, etc. The starch industry employs many chemists. The alfalfa crop affords a rich source of industrial protein, vitamins, pigments, fiber, and unknown materials which chemists are beginning to study. Indeed, the agricultural chemist may find many new ways to utilize agricultural crops through factory processing to obtain products for use in industry as well as for food for man and animals.

Government Opportunities

1. The legal control of foods and feeding stuffs requires municipal, state, and Federal laboratories, staffed by chemists who make chemical and physical tests of the quality of products to insure proper labeling and fitness for intended use. These laboratories employ chemists with various levels of training and experience.

2. The Federal government has established four regional research laboratories for the purpose of finding new uses for agricultural products. Positions in these laboratories are open to properly trained chemists, and already many important discoveries have been made.

3. The state agricultural experiment stations and the United States Department of Agriculture all maintain research laboratories where problems in the various fields of agricultural chemistry are being investigated.

Educational Opportunities

The state agricultural colleges present many opportunities to agricultural chemists, not only in the departments of agricultural chemistry but in other departments, such as animal husbandry, poultry husbandry, horticulture, home economics, and botany, where research problems involving chemistry are under investigation.

Training

A college degree is the key to entering the chemical industry if a person wants to work in research, administration, sales, public relations, or marketing.

The industry generally hires inexperienced workers for processing jobs and trains them on the job. Companies usually prefer to hire high-school graduates for assignment to a labor pool for such jobs as filling drums, moving materials, and helping the skilled chemical operators.

Technicians employed by agricultural chemical firms are qualified for their jobs in many different ways. A person may become a technician by studying at a technical institute or vocational school. He may also qualify by college training, with courses in special areas of his interest. Quite often technicians are persons who dropped out of college before graduation, or graduated from college with some chemistry or other scientific training that led to an interest in the chemical industry.

Training for work in biochemistry often requires education beyond the bachelor's degree. Students working for master's or Ph.D. degrees may be employed as graduate or research assistants.

The biochemist is trained in the chemistry of foods, their utilization, and the physical and chemical changes that take place in animal and plant production. He must have a knowledge of research procedure. Biochemists may be classified as agricultural biochemist, dairy chemist, food technologist, nutritional chemist, plant chemist, control chemist, research biochemist, animal nutritionist, food processor, laboratory technician, and others.

How Do You Become a Biochemist?

Students planning to train for the profession of biochemistry should have a high scholastic record and the ambition to be of service to society. They should be interested in laboratory work, have a keen desire to attain perfection, and have absolute honesty of observation, thought, and judgment.

A bachelor's degree from a four-year course in science is a minimum requirement for employment as a biochemist. The curriculum should be designed to provide a thorough background in mathematics; in physics; in inorganic, organic, analytical, and physical chemistry; and in such fields of biology as bacteriology, botany, and zoology.

The biochemist who is interested in research and wishes to qualify for the most important positions must undertake postgraduate training. Obtaining a master's degree usually requires about two years and the Ph.D. degree about four years of additional study and research after the bachelor's degree has been received.

Employment Outlook

The agricultural chemical industry is expected to provide thousands of job opportunities for new workers during the late 1960s and early 1970s. Many of these openings will result from the expansion of the use of chemicals in the production and preservation of foodstuffs. The career opportunities will probably expand faster than the estimated 20 per cent increase for the nation's total working population, since the industry is one of the nation's most rapidly growing segments of the agricultural area.

Job Descriptions in the Agricultural Chemical Industry

1. *Agricultural Biochemist, Food Control and Research.* Tests raw materials; controls manufacturing processes, and insures uniformly high-grade products. Engages in research to discover better methods of processing; to prevent deterioration of quality in raw materials and processed products; to develop palatability and nutritional values; and to utilize culls, trimmings, hulls, and wastes or by-products.

2. *Agricultural Chemist.* Performs chemical analyses on macro- or micro-amounts of agricultural chemicals such as pesticides, plant growth regulators, and food additives. Develops specific methods for discovering trace amounts of agricultural chemicals which may be present in crops at the time of harvest. Investigates the mode-of-action of pesticides and plant growth regulators, involving the study of enzyme action in plants and animals as well as cell-free systems.

3. *Agricultural Chemurgist.* Tries to convert agricultural products into materials that can be used profitably in industry and to find new ways to utilize wastes, culls, and surpluses; analyzes agricultural products; studies the characteristics of the substances which he isolates and tries to find new and more profitable uses for them by converting them

into textile fibers, paper, plastics, or chemicals that can be used in paints, plastics, fibers, solvents, motor fuels, and others.

4. *Biochemist (Plant).* Investigates the plant biochemical reactions and the factors influencing them. Studies minerals, carbohydrates, enzymes, proteins, nucleic acids, pigments, and other substances found in living plant systems. Discovers and develops the utilization of plant biological products in man's economy and of commercially valuable materials from items of plant biological origin.

5. *Dairy Biochemist.* Conducts research on composition and on chemical and nutritional changes during processing, packaging, and storing of dairy products; provides chemical control over raw materials, processes, and products; analyzes milk, butter, cheese, ice cream, and the materials used in processing dairy products; develops improved techniques and equipment used in manufacturing dairy products and studies the utilization of dairy by-products as food and in industry.

6. *Food and Nutritional Chemist.* Studies the digestibility of foods, their biological values; their composition in respect to proteins, fats, carbohydrates, vitamins, and minerals; the distribution and storage of materials in the body; the chemical reactions occurring in the conversion of food materials into substances found in the body; the waste materials produced as a result of chemical reactions in the body; and the formulation of diets in chemical terms that will meet the requirements for the production of healthy, productive animals.

7. *Food Technology Chemist.* Invents new methods and equipment for the processing of foods in order to provide products of higher food value, better keeping qualities, greater palatability, and lower cost; determines conditions that prevent detrimental nutritional and chemical changes during processing and storage of food products; provides chemical control of factory processes so that suitable raw materials can be selected and products of uniform, high-grade quality manufactured; and gains experience in food manufacturing and merchandising so that he may become a plant manager or an executive.

8. *Laboratory Technician.* Engages in laboratory work under the supervision of someone actively directing a research or service program. This work may be chemical, biochemical, or physiological, or involve any other aspect of laboratories either directly or indirectly connected with agriculture.

9. *Weed Control Specialist.* Furnishes farmers with specifications for the appropriate control of weeds. Analyzes the local flora and suggests methods for the chemical and physical control of noxious shrubs. He must be able to explain his ideas clearly and be especially adept in human relations. He must be able to perform the required testing of new chemicals to control weeds and to enforce Federal and state regulations.

Chapter VIII

Agricultural Education Including Agricultural Extension

Agricultural education is one of the professional areas in the agricultural field. It offers many opportunities for those interested in education as it relates to agriculture. Opportunities for college-trained men in agricultural education have continued to increase during the past several years.

Teaching agriculture in public high schools offers an unusual opportunity to a large number of agricultural college graduates. Vocational agriculture was first established in the high schools in 1917. The teacher of agriculture is a member of the high-school faculty with a high standard of professional and technical training.

Teaching is interesting. In a vocational agriculture class you teach high-school boys, young farmers, and adult farmers. Much of the work is done on the farms of your students. Your teaching will deal with practical farm problems. In a single day an agriculture teacher may make a field trip with a class to select dairy heifers, work in the shop with another class on adjusting combines, and teach still another group new practices of crop fertilization.

The teacher of vocational agriculture enjoys many advantages. His work is interesting, practical, and enjoyable. He receives an income that provides a comfortable living and achieves the highly respected status traditionally accorded teachers by rural communities.

The vocational teacher organizes and instructs young farmers in improving their farming practices. He teaches all phases of agriculture, such as soils, farm crops, animal husbandry, poultry, machinery, engineering, conservation, farm management, and rural living. He lives in the local community and takes an active part in civic affairs. He serves as adviser of the local Future Farmer chapter, and often as adviser to 4-H Clubs. He is employed for twelve months of the year.

He also conducts part-time and evening classes for adult farmers and out-of-school young farmers who desire more agricultural instruction. He is confronted with every conceivable farm problem and advises both students and adults regarding their individual farm problems and practices.

Your Assets

As in most other vocations, there are certain personal qualities that will help one to be happier and more successful in his chosen work. The following four assets will, to a large measure, determine a person's success and future opportunities.

Leadership. Qualities of leadership are essential. You need to be able to lead, guide, counsel, and advise boys. The ability to be a leader gains the respect of those you teach and makes your teaching more productive and enjoyable.

Personality. As a prospective teacher of vocational agriculture you should be able to work harmoniously with many different types of people. A pleasing personality and a cooperative attitude will be invaluable to you in working with your students, fellow teachers, and others in the community.

Scholarship. Students in the upper 50 per cent of their high-school classes are usually most successful in teaching vocational agriculture. It takes a good student to complete the college preparation necessary. The good student is also better able to keep up to date with new agricultural practices after he begins his work as a teacher. He is able to build the undergraduate base for further graduate work, which is more and more a requirement for professional advancement.

Farm Experience. The fact that you have lived and worked on a farm will help you to become a successful teacher of vocational agriculture. As such a teacher, you will need to understand and like farm people, as well as to demonstrate farming practices, and your experience can be put to good use.

Employment Opportunities

The teacher of vocational agriculture is employed by the local board of education for twelve months of the year, although in nonvocational teaching a few agricultural teachers are employed only nine months of the year. The latter job is essentially the same, but without student projects, F.F.A. chapters, and adult evening classes. Nonvocational teachers usually handle additional courses in sciences and industrial arts.

As a teacher the graduate in agriculture should seek to develop the interest and understanding of students in the conservation of natural resources, the importance of agriculture, pride and enjoyment in farming and rural life, the importance of home and family, the economic loss caused by weeds, insects, and diseases, and the improvement of economic and social conditions in the community.

He may go into general or specialized farming or into government work. Many men obtain initial experience in teaching, then become county agricultural agents. They may be employed by the Farm Bureau as local specialists in recreation leadership or educational promotion, or advance in extension work to the state level in some specialized field. They may become soil conservationists, farm credit agents, or sales representatives in the business field.

A general training in education also fits one to become an agricultural missionary—to teach in countries unfamiliar with modern agricultural practices. He must learn the language spoken in the country where he works, and he must be able to teach all aspects of agriculture. He is usually sponsored and employed by a church organization.

Training

Training of teachers has been limited during recent years, as instructors have migrated to other fields. More schools desire to add vocational agriculture departments, and thus there are many opportunities for employment and a bright future for all graduates in agricultural education.

A bachelor's degree, a background of farm experience, a teaching certificate, and acceptable personal characteristics are necessary to enter teaching or its many allied professions.

Salary

Since vocational agriculture teachers are employed the year round, salaries compare favorably with those of other teachers in the public schools. The pay is increased according to experience, training, and demonstrated ability, and an allowance is provided for travel expenses.

Agricultural Extension Service

Have you heard the expression "See your county agent" when someone wants information on a better farming practice, a new crop variety, or improved livestock feeding? Have you belonged to a 4-H Club or watched a club member demonstrate how to fit a dairy calf? Or has your father ever taken part in a series of meetings on improving the family farm?

All of these—and many more activities—are examples of the work of the Agricultural Extension Service. Actually, Agricultural Extension provides teaching outside the laboratory and outside the classroom. It brings the results of the latest research in farming and homemaking directly to the farmer, his wife, and his sons and daughters.

In 1914, roughly half a century after the establishment of the Land-Grant Colleges "for the benefit of agriculture and the mechanical arts," steps were taken on a national scale to make available to farmers the vast store of scientific information developed by these colleges and by the Agricultural Experiment Stations. In that year, Congress enacted provisions for an arrangement between the U.S. Department of Agriculture and the Land-Grant Colleges whereby any state could match Federal funds in order to establish cooperative agricultural extension work. The purpose was to give instruction and practical demonstrations in agriculture and home economics to persons not in attendance in agricultural colleges—*i.e.,* to the operating farmers and their families. Today there are about 12,000 paid agricultural extension workers at county, state, and Federal levels, and the service extends into nearly every agricultural county in the nation.

Basically, the work of the county agricultural agent is to provide educational and advisory service in agriculture and home economics to rural and other families. Administratively, he is responsible for the county agricultural extension program, the effectiveness of which depends upon the cooperation of farmer committees and many volunteers in adult-education and youth-club work. His salary is paid jointly by the Agriculture Extension Service and by the state in which he works.

The county agent works for and with rural people of all ages. He distributes information and instructions concerning improved methods of agriculture by means of demonstrations, individual guidance, group meetings, tours, lectures, and discussions and through the press and radio. In order to be able to advise farmers concerning problems such as crops, rotation, varieties of seed, fertilization, soil conservation, livestock production, drainage, machinery, and marketing, he keeps abreast of the latest scientific developments provided by the agricultural colleges and experiment stations.

No one man can have a thorough knowledge of all aspects of so complex and diversified a field as modern agriculture. Credit for our agricultural progress must be given largely to the agricultural extension workers, who have shown farmers the way to better themselves and their farms. To supplement his own knowledge of agricultural problems, the agent is able to call upon any of the specialists of the State Extension Staff. Often such an extension specialist is a former county agent who has done graduate work and demonstrated outstanding ability in one or more particular fields. He may have specialized in agricultural education, soils, dairy, poultry, marketing problems, or one of a dozen areas.

Other members of the local extension service are the home demonstration agents and assistant agents. Their responsibilities are similar to those of the county agricultural agent. In some counties, the 4-H Club work still is performed by the county agent himself, but in more and more states it is becoming the practice to employ a separate agent whose chief duty is the supervision of older youth and 4-H groups. Among other duties he conducts training programs for advisers and officers, coaches demonstration and judging teams, and plans and operates camps for 4-H Club members.

Others on the State Extension Staff include administrators, supervisors, and state leaders, who are responsible for administration of state extension programs and supervision of personnel.

How to Qualify for Extension Work

A minimum requirement for the job of county agent is a bachelor's degree from a college of agriculture. Many county agents hold higher degrees. In general, it is desirable to take courses providing a broad background in agriculture, rather than to specialize too narrowly at the undergraduate level. Basic subjects which should be emphasized are chemistry and biology; other helpful courses are agricultural economics, psychology, principles of education, teaching methods, English composition, agricultural journalism, and public speaking. The agricultural education or agricultural economics curriculum, or any other agricultural program, supplemented by special courses in extension methods, would be well suited to students planning to enter extension work.

Personal qualifications for extension work are as important as educational background. The person who does not genuinely enjoy working with people will not be happy in agricultural extension work; the person who lacks enthusiasm, persuasive ability, and persistence will not be successful. The successful extension worker likes rural people and in most cases has a farm background himself. He has an even disposition and is not easily discouraged when farmers are cautious and deliberate in accepting the new ideas he presents. His health must be consistently good, and he must have the stamina to sustain him on a job that entails not only daytime but evening meetings and much travel.

The Outlook for Employment

A student who has enrolled in a college of agriculture with a view to entering extension service should discuss his plans with an adviser not later than the end of his freshman year. He may be able to gain experience on a part-time basis while in college, as an assistant agent, perhaps in 4-H Club leadership work. The entering job in extension service is usually that of assistant county extension agent. He will advance to the position of county agent through experience and merit, or he may transfer to some related field. The availability of jobs in extension work depends largely upon the annual rate of turnover (retirement or transfer of experienced personnel) and upon the budget for additional personnel in the service. From a long-range point of view, the field of agricultural extension is expanding both in numbers employed and in geographical scope, but this expansion is not rapid.

Many enter the field after successful experience in agricultural education. Experience as a county agent provides an excellent background for transfer into such related fields as agricultural business or industry, especially in sales work; higher-level advisory or administrative work in agricultural agencies; or teaching in agricultural colleges, after graduate training.

For additional information regarding the county agricultural agent, consult the Agricultural Extension Service or the dean of the college of agriculture in your state.

Job Descriptions in Agricultural Education and Extension

1. *Agricultural Teacher—Vocational Agriculture.* Teaches vocational agriculture under the auspices of the public schools in accord-

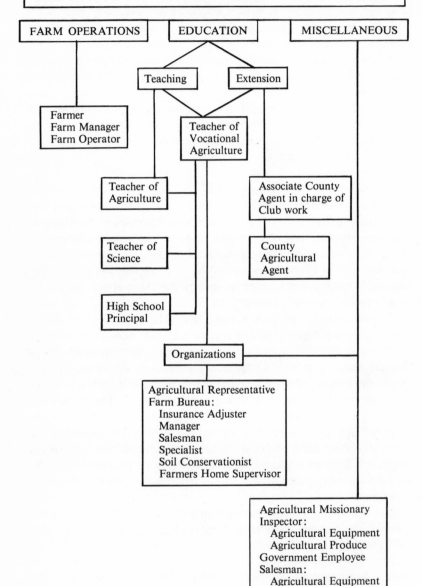

OPPORTUNITIES FOR MAJORS IN AGRICULTURAL EDUCATION

FARM OPERATIONS

EDUCATION

MISCELLANEOUS

Teaching

Extension

Farmer
Farm Manager
Farm Operator

Teacher of
Vocational
Agriculture

Teacher of
Agriculture

Associate County
Agent in charge of
Club work

Teacher of
Science

County
Agricultural
Agent

High School
Principal

Organizations

Agricultural Representative
Farm Bureau:
    Insurance Adjuster
    Manager
    Salesman
    Specialist
    Soil Conservationist
    Farmers Home Supervisor

Agricultural Missionary
Inspector:
    Agricultural Equipment
    Agricultural Produce
Government Employee
Salesman:
    Agricultural Equipment
    Agricultural Supplies
    Agricultural Seeds

ance with provisions of the Federal Smith-Hughes and George Barden acts. Gives instruction in all-day schools or departments, or in day-unit classes, to youths of high-school age. Conducts evening classes for adult farmers. In summer supervises students' farm practice. Sponsors Future Farmers of America organization. As a community leader, renders special service in agriculture and assists in rural community undertakings.

2. *Teacher of Agriculture, High School.* Teaches classes in agriculture, usually with additional courses in science or industrial arts. The extent of practical work (projects) carried on by the pupils is optional, since the instruction is not under Federal supervision. It is more like regular academic high-school teaching.

3. *Teacher of Agronomy, College.* As an agronomist, usually a specialist in some subarea of agronomy, devotes much of his time to teaching college students. Directs and evaluates research projects and research facilities. Must have teaching ability and should also be able to develop interest and enthusiasm in his students.

4. *Teacher of Animal Science, College.* Gives instruction in the judging, breeding, feeding, and management of livestock. Employed by agricultural colleges at home and abroad.

5. *Vocational Agriculture (Vo-Ag) Teacher, High School.* Teaches high-school classes for pupils who plan to farm, engage in agricultural occupations related to farming, or attend agricultural colleges. Plans and prepares courses of study, supervises projects of pupils on farms, provides on-farm individual instruction. Advises and supervises chapters of Future Farmers of America. Counsels and advises students interested in preparing for agricultural occupations.

6. *County Agricultural Agent.* As county director of educational programs in agriculture, works out of the state agricultural college in cooperation with the state agricultural experiment station and the U.S. Department of Agriculture. Distributes information and instructions concerning improved methods of agriculture to the county rural population. Gives advice on farm problems; supervises 4-H Clubs, often through an associate county agent.

7. *Associate County Agent.* Supervises 4-H Clubs and older rural youth groups, securing and maintaining memberships, helping to organize clubs, assisting in club programs, training advisers and club officers, following up club activities. County activities include planning and holding conferences; training demonstrators and judging teams;

working with other agents, civic groups, and schools; planning and conducting camps, contests, exhibits, and achievement programs; assuming civic responsibilities in county and community. Works under supervision of county agent.

8. *Agricultural Extension Specialist.* Is a leader of the Federal Extension Program. Helps state extension directors, supervisors, and program leaders to plan, develop, and coordinate national, regional, and state extension programs. Helps develop and maintain relationships on extension work with officials of state and territorial Land-Grant Colleges and Universities and with the heads of public and private agencies. Directs the work of program leaders or specialists in specific fields, such as agriculture, home economics, rural youth (4-H Clubs and work with young men and women), agricultural economics, marketing, and rural sociology. Assists state extension personnel to plan, develop, and coordinate national, regional, and state educational programs.

9. *Agricultural Extension Specialist (Agronomy).* For the Agricultural Extension Service, performs such duties as developing and conducting educational work in agronomy and related programs, including the preparation of information and materials for use by state extension agronomists and county extension workers. Is responsible for developing national and regional programs. Requires a B.S. degree in agriculture or four years' experience, or a combination, plus experience in extension work with specialization in agronomy.

10. *Agricultural Extension Specialist (Cooperative Programs).* For the Agricultural Extension Service, examines and coordinates extension programs of the State Extension Services; or represents the U.S. in foreign countries in establishing or developing extension work relative to cooperative agricultural programs. Same basic qualifications as above, plus experience in extension work with specialization in administration.

11. *Agricultural Extension Specialist (Field Studies and Training).* For the U.S. Department of Agriculture, plans, organizes, and conducts educational research in all phases of cooperative extension work carried on by State Extension Services; plans, organizes, and conducts training programs for extension service employees; coordinates educational research and training programs conducted through state and regional centers. Same basic qualifications as above, plus experience

in agricultural extension education with emphasis on field studies and training.

12. *Agricultural Extension Specialist (4-H Club Agent).* Represents the Extension Service of the U.S. Department of Agriculture in a region of approximately twelve states. Helps plan, supervise, and administer 4-H Club programs.

13. *Pomology Extension Specialist.* Employed by a state university or the Civil Service. Holds meetings and gives individual instruction to fruit growers to keep them informed of recent developments in pomology research and to assist them in carrying out these practices.

14. *Agriculturist.* For the U.S. Department of Agriculture, administers, supervises, or conducts extension work in the general field of agriculture or in one or more of its specialized branches. May work at home or abroad. Must meet educational qualifications for county agent or have had at least four years of experience in the field, or a combination of the two, plus specialized experience depending on the level of the job.

15. *Agricultural Aid.* Assists professional research workers in carrying out experiments in agronomy, animal husbandry, or other branches of agriculture; performs the manual labor and routine duties necessary to care for animals, plants, and crops; tills the soil; collects and preserves seed or harvest and weighs and stores crops according to the nature of the research.

16. *Agricultural Consultant.* Consults with and advises individuals, organizations, or companies on agricultural matters in the particular field in which he specializes, such as agronomy, agricultural engineering, or soil conservation.

17. *Agricultural Missionary.* Directs agricultural education in a country unfamiliar with modern practices. Must be familiar with all types of agricultural practices, crops, livestock, and social aspects and must possess broad practical experience in dealing with people. A knowledge of the language spoken in the country of employment is necessary.

18. *Farm Bureau Specialist.* Promotes the activities of the Farm Bureau in his special field. Common fields are those of rural recreation leadership, direction of youth groups in the Farm Bureau, and educational promotion of the various special fields.

19. *Farm Manager.* For the owner, organizes and directs soil and

cropping systems and other enterprises on one or more farms. May supervise several foremen. Frequently works on a commission or bonus basis, in which case he usually has extensive control over farming activities and administration policy. The time devoted to managing as contrasted to performing the farm operations will depend upon the size of the unit; the larger the unit, the greater the portion of time given to the managing function.

20. *Farm Operator.* Is in charge of crop and livestock production, soil management, buying supplies, and selling products. Must be an able-bodied worker and must exercise good judgment as to the time of performing the various tasks. The farm operator and his family live on the farm as well as work there.

21. *Salesman, Farm and Garden Equipment and Supplies.* Sells farm and garden supplies, such as farm implements and machinery, feed, fertilizer, and seed, and performs other duties associated with any business. May work in private industry, in a farm cooperative, or purchase a private business, such as a grain elevator, hardware store, hatchery, etc.

22. *Farmers Home Administration Supervisor.* At the county level, supervises the work of the F.H.A., which makes loans to persons who cannot borrow money through regular loan agencies. Investigates applicants; assists with securing of livestock, machinery, and supplies; visits clients; recommends farm programs; and collects loan payments. Successful experience as teacher, farmer, or businessman is desirable.

Chapter IX

Agricultural Engineering

Agricultural engineering is the application of any and all branches of engineering to farming, rural life, the processing of farm products, and such allied activities as wildlife conservation and rural recreation. It draws largely on mechanical, electrical, structural, civil, and hydraulic engineering.

At one time there were only two kinds of engineering—military and civil, or the engineering of war and peace. As engineering grew, it was divided into branches based on its principal content. The term civil engineering was confined to fixed works such as roads, bridges, dams, and other structures which had to stand still and resist motion. Mechanical engineering was that of motion—machines and mechanisms of all sorts, including engines and other prime movers. Then came electrical engineering, centering around the generation, distribution, and application of electric energy. These are examples of the fundamental branches of engineering.

To a large extent engineering has again been reclassified, but still according to application. This is a practical expedient—simply a grouping together of any and all kinds of engineering that are used in a certain industry or by a man in some field of work. Thus mining engineering is mechanical in its cars, pumps, and hoists; electrical in its motors, lights, and wiring; civil as to its work in earth and rock; and chemical in certain ore treatments. Similarly, automotive engineering consists mainly of mechanical and electrical engineering.

Agricultural engineering is a profession, with its parts interwoven and bound together because all apply to a single industry, and often to single farms. Yet it may help you to see the picture of the things that agricultural engineers do if you look at them in the technical classifications used by the American Society of Agricultural Engineers. They are practical divisions, based not so much on the logic of the subject matter as on the specialization of many members within the profession.

67

Agricultural engineering involves the application of the principles of engineering and of agricultural science to the problems of agriculture. Agricultural engineering may be divided into the major divisions representing:

1. Power—Specification of the power requirements for the machines and processes of agriculture.
2. Machines—Functional and mechanical requirements of machines to do the work of agriculture.
3. Structures—To provide control of environment for maximum biological efficiency.
4. Water—To meet the needs of the growing plant, the animal, and the rural people.
5. Processing—Engineering methods of increasing the value of biological materials.
6. Transport—Engineering of methods of handling biological materials.
7. Systems—Integration of water, power, machines, structures, and processes into optimum systems.

Fields of Specialization

Agricultural Machines and Power. This specialty includes the design, the development through research, the manufacture, and the demonstration of the proper use of: (1) farm field machines for tillage, weed control, planting and seeding, insect and plant disease control, harvesting, and other field practices; (2) crop-processing and -handling machinery such as corn shellers, feed grinders, silage cutters, etc.; (3) drainage and irrigation machinery; (4) equipment for stump and stone removal; (5) internal combustion engines, generating equipment motors, and accessories as a source of farm power; and (6) tractors, and other transport equipment, as well as care, repair, and maintenance of mechanical farm equipment.

Farm Structures and Utilities. This specialty deals with the planning, design, arrangement, and construction of farm buildings and structures, including dwellings, and their adaptation to specific regions, types of farming, and economic conditions.

The engineer is concerned with structures as functional units that provide adequate dwellings for farm operators and efficient animal housing, crop storage, shelter for supplies and equipment, and facilities for handling and processing agricultural products.

The specialty also includes the development, design, and proper use of equipment and utilities in farm buildings. It involves the requirements of the farmstead with respect to arrangement, fencing, water supply, sanitation, and sewage disposal. The design of prefabricated structures and special types of buildings for feed handling, milling, dehydration, and refrigeration are engineering activities for this subdivision.

Objectives in farm-structures engineering are the improvement of environmental conditions, economy, adequate structural qualities, labor-use efficiency, and the conservation of feed, stored products, and animals.

Soil and Water Conservation. This specialty deals with the engineering design, layout, construction, and maintenance of structures and measures for soil-erosion control and conservation, use, management, and disposal of water as related to agricultural lands.

Soil-erosion control involves preventive and corrective structures and measures as terraces, diversions, waterways, and check dams.

Water conservation includes the holding of water on the land by contour cultivation ridges, furrows, and pit or basin cultivation, and the impounding of water in ponds or reservoirs.

Irrigation involves the pumping of water from wells or its diversion from streams or reservoirs; measuring water and delivering it to farms; and development and use of efficient methods of applying water. Consideration must be given to topography, land-use capabilities, the quantity and quality of water available, and the economic feasibility.

Drainage is essential in most irrigated areas, is needed to achieve maximum production from cultivated lands with poor surface or internal drainage, and may make possible the reclamation of inherently productive lands now in swamps or marshes. Drainage may require the improvement of natural streams, or the use of open ditches, tile, pumping, or combinations of these methods as required by topographic, soil, or cultural factors, and of appurtenant structures.

Flood control for the protection of agricultural lands involves the improvement of vegetative cover, the retention of water by conservation structures and measures, the detention of water in flood-control reservoirs, and the use of diversions and levees.

All of these activities require the application of engineering knowledge and procedures to the solution of agricultural problems, in collaboration with other engineers and agricultural technicians.

Rural Electrification. This specialty includes the design and layout of wiring and lighting for farmsteads and farm buildings; productive uses of power, light, heat, ultraviolet and other forms of electric energy in agriculture; the design, construction, testing, installation, operation, care, and repair of electrically powered, heated, lighted, energized, or controlled farm equipment and processes, water systems, and water heaters; and the design, testing, construction, and installation of major items of household equipment such as food dehydrators, refrigerators, dryers, heating devices, etc. Much of the work in this field has consisted in the construction, development, introduction, and economic study of electrical farm equipment.

Processing of Farm Products. This specialty deals with the application of engineering methods, equipment, and machinery to the processing of various types of crops and animal products. It includes research, design, manufacture, and application of special processing equipment for pasteurization, canning, milling, freezing, curing, and grading of all types of agricultural commodities, including dairy products, animal products, seed, grain, poultry, fruit, vegetables, and specialty crops.

Opportunities for Agricultural Engineers

Because agricultural engineering is a rapidly growing profession, persons acquiring such training are in great demand. As is currently the case in other fields of endeavor, such as electronics or nuclear engineering, the present demand for agricultural engineers exceeds the available supply.

A choice of work in agricultural engineering is almost unlimited because of the wide variety of opportunities. A person holding a degree in agricultural engineering will be able to do satisfying, professional, and rewarding work in the city or in a rural environment. He is qualified for:

Development and testing of new or improved equipment for tillage, harvesting, and processing crops and for saving labor on the farm.
Planning and layout of tile and open-ditch drainage systems, irri-

gation systems, terraces, strip-cropping, grass waterways, and other soil conservation practices.

Design and construction of farm machinery, farm buildings, and electrical conveniences.

Promotion and sale of a wide variety of engineering equipment and materials used on the farm.

Management positions with large farms, canning companies, rural electrification cooperatives, and manufacturing companies.

Research work in industry, education, and government with new methods and equipment for saving labor, increasing crop yield and quality, and improving farm living.

Extension work in industry and public service, including work in foreign service.

Training in Agricultural Engineering

The agricultural engineering curriculum at a large number of Land-Grant Colleges and Universities offers an opportunity for training in the physical sciences and in basic engineering, in addition to courses in agricultural engineering. A wide choice of courses enables one to specialize in a particular phase of the field.

The agricultural engineering curriculum leads to the degree of Bachelor of Agricultural Engineering. This degree, like degrees in other fields of engineering, is recognized by employers seeking men trained as engineers in agriculture.

As a recognized profession with its own specialized education, agricultural engineering is one of the youngest. It remained for some of the younger states in a young nation to set up separate courses in agricultural engineering. In 1907, the American Society of Agricultural Engineers was founded by about a dozen men who met for the purpose at the University of Wisconsin.

While instruction in agricultural engineering had been going on for some years, it was not until 1910 that any institution conferred the degree of bachelor of science in agricultural engineering. (The bachelor's degree is the standard for full-course graduates in all branches of engineering.) By 1925 there were ten and now there are forty-five institutions giving such training and degree, or its equivalent; and more than twenty-five of the professional curricula in agricultural engineering offered by these schools have been accredited by the Engineers Council for Professional Development, a nationally recognized accrediting agency. Many of them also give graduate instruction leading to the master's degree (M.S.) in agricultural engineering. Also, programs directed toward the doctor of philosophy degree (Ph.D.) may be arranged in several departments of agricultural engineering.

The professional curricula in agricultural engineering offered by the various institutions are strikingly similar, because experience has shown pretty well "what it takes" to train a well-qualified agricultural engineer. This is especially true of the fundamental sciences, such as mathematics, mechanics, and agriculture. In the advanced courses and specialties you may find more differences among the various colleges, for every institution has something for which it is famous. In general, however, you will find what you want at the college of agriculture in your own state or a nearby state.

Training in Mechanized Farming

Should you be interested in training for sales promotion or service activities in farm equipment, materials, and facilities, or in farm management and operation, the colleges of agriculture offer a four-year course with a major in mechanized farming. This course of study is somewhat less technical and more practical than the agricultural engineering curriculum and leads to the bachelor of science degree in agriculture.

For further information write or visit the college of agriculture in your state or a nearby state.

Less Than College Degree

The farm mechanic is not an agricultural engineer, but he is needed wherever agricultural engineering is applied. The farm mechanic assists the agricultural engineer to solve agricultural problems in crop and livestock production, harvesting, processing, storage, transportation, and soil and water conservation. The designing and developing of new agricultural machinery and farm buildings and the use of electricity and other mechanized farm equipment are bringing about a change in the servicing of the machinery used on the present-day farm.

The farm mechanic works on farm tractors, garden tractors, and such agricultural machinery and equipment as pumps, irrigation equipment, cultivators, sprayers, dusters, harvesting machinery, and numerous other devices used in soil preparation, in planting and cultivating the crops, and in spraying, dusting, and harvesting hay, forage, grain, and vegetables. He may also assist in laying out and supervising the construction of farm buildings, utilities, and crop-processing plants and in laying out contours for conserving soil and water by the installation of irrigation facilities, drainage systems, and flood and soil-erosion control programs.

His major contribution to the farm is servicing the power equipment used in planting, cultivating, harvesting, and processing farm crops. Many of the modern tractors and harvesting equipment cost thousands of dollars and require highly trained mechanics to service the diesel motors and the hydraulic systems.

Steady jobs are generally found in machinery distributors' service shops. Farm mechanics are also employed by commercial farms, machinery companies, farm power companies, companies that design and erect farm structures, farm utilities, oil companies, farm management agencies, supply companies, and processing plants. A large number of farm mechanics have their own shops.

Personal Qualifications. The basic qualification needed to become a farm mechanic is actual farm operation experience with mechanical aptitude and a reasonable knowledge of agriculture and the economic problems involved. Today no company will accept an applicant for training unless he is a high-school graduate.

The necessary training is often secured by working with experienced mechanics and with equipment on the farm. High schools teaching vocational agriculture and mechanics play an important role in the early training of a person who wants to become a farm mechanic.

Good physical condition is usually necessary in order to handle the outdoor as well as the indoor requirements of the job. Good vision and an acceptable personal appearance are valuable assets.

Method of Entry

Talk your plans over with your parents, your high-school counselor, and with the owner or manager of a local implement dealership. If possible, visit the employment office of a tractor and farm machinery manufacturer.

The basic requirement for this occupation is interest in working with farm machinery and other farm equipment. A reasonable general knowledge of the principles of mechanics will help a person find employment. The person who has demonstrated his reliability and an aptitude in a community may find employment in one of the local agricultural implement businesses as a trainee. Since the nature of the work is such that most operations must be carried on with a high degree of accuracy, the farm mechanic can demonstrate his reliability during the training period.

The person interested in mechanics may work part-time during his high-school training on a neighboring farm, in a local implement service center, and on machinery on the home farm. The experience of repairing and adjusting engines will assist in determining an interest in mechanical work. The would-be farm mechanic should have completed high school or have taken equal training in a trade school specializing in some phase of mechanics, basic electricity, welding, blueprint reading, and auto or shop mechanics. Machine-shop operations such as layout work and drill press work would be helpful. A larger number of the implement companies provide a manufacturers service school to develop skills essential for servicing their equipment.

Job Descriptions in Agricultural Engineering

1. *Agricultural Engineer.* Applies engineering principles to solve agricultural problems in production, processing, transportation, and handling. Designs, develops, and supervises the manufacturing of agricultural machinery such as pumps, irrigation equipment, tractors, cultivators, sprayers, dusters, and harvesters. Lays out and supervises construction of farm buildings and utilities, crop-processing plants, and rural electric power distribution systems. Conserves soil and water by installation of irrigation, drainage, and flood and soil-erosion control systems. May specialize in such fields as farm management, pest control, rural roads, and farm fire protection and safety. Designs food-processing equipment; operates and manages food-processing plants. May also specialize in research, extension, consulting, inspecting, testing, teaching at the university level, technical writing and editing, or technical sales and service.

2. *Agricultural Electrification Engineer.* Utilizes electricity in the field of agriculture; consults with rural families in such areas as wiring, layout and wire size, types of electric motor to use, heating cable, and air-conditioning. Aids in selection of wiring, switches, automatic controls, and special motors for such jobs as feed grinding, forage and feed handling, and crop drying.

3. *Agricultural Irrigation Engineer.* Applies basic engineering in-

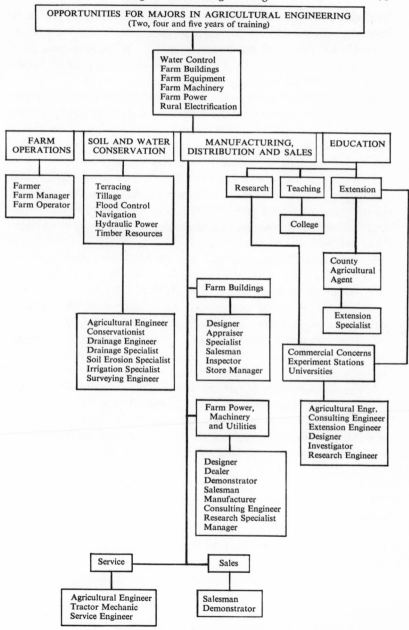

OPPORTUNITIES FOR MAJORS IN AGRICULTURAL ENGINEERING
(Two, four and five years of training)

Water Control
Farm Buildings
Farm Equipment
Farm Machinery
Farm Power
Rural Electrification

FARM OPERATIONS

SOIL AND WATER CONSERVATION

MANUFACTURING, DISTRIBUTION AND SALES

EDUCATION

Farmer
Farm Manager
Farm Operator

Terracing
Tillage
Flood Control
Navigation
Hydraulic Power
Timber Resources

Research

Teaching

Extension

College

County Agricultural Agent

Extension Specialist

Agricultural Engineer
Conservationist
Drainage Engineer
Drainage Specialist
Soil Erosion Specialist
Irrigation Specialist
Surveying Engineer

Farm Buildings

Designer
Appraiser
Specialist
Salesman
Inspector
Store Manager

Commercial Concerns
Experiment Stations
Universities

Farm Power, Machinery and Utilities

Agricultural Engr.
Consulting Engineer
Extension Engineer
Designer
Investigator
Research Engineer

Designer
Dealer
Demonstrator
Salesman
Manufacturer
Consulting Engineer
Research Specialist
Manager

Service

Sales

Agricultural Engineer
Tractor Mechanic
Service Engineer

Salesman
Demonstrator

formation to the problem of supplying irrigation water to the farm. Supervises construction of ditches, pipe lines, ponds, and dams. Is responsible for design of the irrigation layout, including pump, pipe, land-surface formation, rate of water application, and sizes and types of engines or motors used as a source of power.

4. *Agricultural Machinery Engineer*. Applies engineering principles to the problem of agricultural machinery use and design. Designs, constructs, and tests agricultural machinery. Advises users of farm machinery as to the size and kinds needed for a certain enterprise. May service and maintain agricultural machinery on large farms.

5. *Agricultural Research Engineer*. Conducts phases of agricultural engineering research concerned with farm machinery, buildings, drainage or water control, or rural electrification; improving present products, discovering new products, and developing processing machinery. Plans and executes experimental work.

6. *Agricultural Safety Engineer*. Is responsible for safety programs in agriculture. Works with farmers, machinery dealers, and county and state officials to promote safety on the farm. Organizes and sponsors safety campaigns at the community and county level. Works with other safety organizations to encourage rural family safety.

7. *Farm Building Designer*. An agricultural engineer; designs houses, barns, garages, poultry houses, implement buildings, milk houses, and other farm buildings; makes drawings of proposed buildings; writes descriptions for use in construction; consults with builder and farmer regarding needs, design, and construction.

8. *Surveying Engineer—Agriculture*. Supervises, directs, and is responsible for the accuracy of engineering land surveys for purposes of construction, map-making, land valuation, or others.

Chapter X

Agricultural Science and Research

It is difficult to separate the opportunities in science and research because of their close relationship. The population of this country is increasing at the rate of more than 3,000,000 a year. To maintain an adequate supply of food and promote the use of better diets, our food industries will require a scientific agricultural research program.

Approximately $125,000,000 is being invested annually by the food industry alone in research on foods produced by the farmer which it processes for distribution. This research includes development of new products, improvement in quality and production of raw materials, location of processing facilities in relation to supply sources and markets, and improvement of transportation, handling, and marketing.

At the present time about $600,000,000 a year is being spent on farm research by the Federal and state governments and by industry.

The colleges of agriculture are graduating young men with training in such areas as animal science, agricultural chemistry, dairy technology, agricultural economics, agricultural education, agronomy, horticulture, poultry, and a dozen others that place our science and research in agriculture at the top of all industry.

The expansion of agricultural aid to foreign countries will create new opportunities for young people interested in science and research.

Science

The young man or woman who is interested in the physical or biological sciences is climbing the stairway to success in agriculture and related areas. There are many opportunities for young people in the various areas of science as they relate to agriculture. Industry and business are continually developing new products, machinery, supplies, and conveniences for use on the farm and in the home. Scientists will be needed in years ahead to find new uses for agricultural products and to continue the research for ways to produce more efficiently.

77

You may ask, "How can I know whether I should train for employment in a scientific career?" Young people are encouraged to talk with scientists and personnel responsible for employing young scientists and to consult their high-school libraries for information regarding opportunities in the various fields of science. They are also encouraged to seek summer employment and to talk with scientists, salesmen, and management regarding the opportunities and training needed to become successful in their chosen fields.

Agriculturally trained people are being called upon by agriculture and its related areas to aid in the production, transportation, processing, and distribution of foods. The need for such trained personnel is a pressing problem at this time. Scientists are responsible for the development of new strains of plants, food processing and preservation techniques, improved methods of storing, and transportation to local centers for distribution.

The training for employment in science is made up of two parts: a general education, and a special or technical education. Frequently, a four-year agricultural graduate adds a fifth year to his training before seeking employment, after which he is immediately qualified to conduct research in the field of his specialization. Sometimes an interest in science as a career begins in high school when the student becomes acquainted with chemistry, physics, mathematics, and the basic fundamentals.

The stairway to success in the agricultural industry finds young men and women on practically every step from the bottom to the top. There is always a place for the young man who is willing to devote time and energy to the fundamentals and to approach his education with enthusiasm.

Research

Research is the process of critical inquiry or examination in seeking facts or principles. It may be extremely simple or highly complex.

The high-school student who enjoys chemistry and mathematics can find many wonderful opportunities for a career in agricultural research.

The success and happiness of a person depend upon his finding a profession that is interesting and challenging. High-school graduates who enjoy working with "things" can find an abundance of opportunities in such areas as agricultural biochemistry, food technology (sometimes called food engineering), food processing, animal, dairy, or poultry sciences, agronomy, horticulture, dairy technology, zoology, botany, or agricultural economics. These specialties offered by the colleges of agriculture train young people to seek new facts, make something useful out of the unknown, create visible objects out of the invisible, develop useful products out of discarded and waste products, make things work that never worked before, find new markets and better products for all markets.

The Need for Trained Scientists

The striking increase in the productivity of American farms today is no accident. It is the result of research programs conducted by Agricultural Experiment Stations, by the Federal government, and by industry. To continue and expand the present research, 3,000 trained young scientists with an agricultural college education are needed annually.

Research is an evolutionary process. It starts with an idea or a problem. This idea or problem is then studied and explored in search for a key to a useful approach. As research is undertaken, the data accumulated are tabulated, summarized, and interpreted. Theories and hypotheses are formulated, and recommendations are drawn.

Agricultural research has followed this general pattern. It differs from pure research in that some possibility of practical application usually is foreseen.

The terms "basic" and "applied" research are familiar, but it is often difficult to apply one or the other term exclusively to any one area. There is no clear-cut line of demarcation between basic and applied research.

Gregor Mendel probably did not realize that from his work on smooth and wrinkled seeds would come the basic laws of heredity. Louis Pasteur did not foresee the far-reaching significance of his discovery that food exposed to the air becomes contaminated with bacteria. Waksman probably never dreamed that his work in soil microbiology would lead to the discovery of streptomycin. Shalk never suspected that his work on sweet clover disease would pave the way for the discovery by Lind of the chemical courmarin, which is so effective in the treatment of coronary thrombosis.

No one doubts that the investment in agricultural research has paid big dividends. It is said that our agricultural knowledge has increased more in the past seventy-five years than in all previous history. We do know that crop yields have increased 50 per cent in the past thirty years; that top dairy herds produce 100 per cent more milk than the average herd; that superior hens lay 90 per cent more eggs than average hens; and that within sixty years the overall efficiency of farming has tripled. And all this progress occurred during periods of great national crisis and when the proportion of city to rural residents was undergoing a complete reversal.

Agricultural research is one of the most attractive of all professional careers. The agricultural scientist works with plants, animals, substances, and distribution of products needed in a complex society. The development of insecticides, fungicides, herbicides, soil conditioners, fertilizers, antibodies, and hundreds of other items are but a small part of his responsibility in helping to develop new and useful products to improve our standard of living.

Job Descriptions in Science and Research

1. *Animal Scientist.* Conducts research in selection, breeding, feeding, management, and marketing of beef and dual-purpose cattle, horses, mules, sheep, hogs, goats, and pet animals. Carries out experiments to determine feed requirements of animals under varying conditions of work or production. Develops improved practices in housing, sanitation, and control of parasites and disease. Develops improved strains of animals through controlled breeding practices. May specialize in a type of animal, such as horses or swine, or in a particular activity, such as breeding or nutrition.

2. *Animal Nutritionist.* Plans and conducts investigations in livestock nutrition. Determines composition of important feedstuffs, compiles rations, tests performance of animals on different rations, conducts grazing trials and metabolism studies. Determines the interrelationships among different nutrients. Studies nutrient imbalances, deficiencies, and toxicities. Develops alternate systems of livestock production.

3. *Animal Pathologist.* Specializes in pathological conditions related to animal nutrition and/or environment; conducts basic research in the field of nutritionally created pathological conditions.

4. *Animal Physiologist.* Specializes in the physiology of animal reproduction. Conducts research to determine and control the factors

influencing efficiency and rate of reproduction and in the fields of artificial insemination, ova transplants, and semen evaluation and preservation. Studies hormone interactions, deficiencies, and imbalances and the role of hormones and related substances in reproduction.

5. *Entomologist—Research.* Studies insects and their relation to crops and to man. May specialize in a particular insect or group of insects, such as boll weevils or leaf hoppers. Develops methods of control or eradication by spraying, dusting, quarantine, or other means; performs laboratory and field work; prepares and publishes reports.

6. *Field Crop Scientist.* Undertakes basic investigations of the physical, chemical, and biological situations, processes, and responses in soils and field crops. Specializes in a subarea of agronomic science, such as soil chemistry, soil fertility, soil physics, physical chemistry of soils, soil biology, soil genesis and morphology, soil conservation, soil management, field crop physiology, field crop ecology, field crop genetics, field crop breeding, seed production, field crop management, and experimental methods in agronomy.

7. *Forest Ecologist.* Conducts research in environmental factors affecting forests. Conducts studies to determine what environmental conditions account for the prevalence of different varieties of trees. Studies biology of different species, including their classification, life history, light and soil requirements, and resistance to insects and disease. Conducts investigations and experiments to determine adaptability of different species to new environmental conditions, such as change in soil type, climate, and altitude.

8. *Forest Pathologist.* Conducts research on the causes of tree diseases and devises methods of control. Research, principally at experiment stations, is conducted on the life histories, requirements, and epidemiology of fungi, bacteria, and viruses and on both direct and indirect control measures. Diseases are studied in forest nurseries, plantations, and natural forest stands. Pathologists at the Forest Products Laboratory study the stains and decays that attack forest products in storage, in transit, and in use. A small number of forest pathologists are assigned to forest and range experiment stations, with headquarters at Upper Darby, Pennsylvania; Asheville, North Carolina; and New Orleans, Louisiana; and at the Forest Products

Laboratories at Madison, Wisconsin; Columbus, Ohio; St. Paul, Minnesota; Fort Collins, Colorado; Berkeley, California; and Portland, Oregon.

9. *Geneticist.* Studies inheritance and variation of characteristics in all forms of life; performs scientific experiments to determine laws, mechanisms, and environmental factors involved in origin, transmission, and development of inherited traits. Analyzes determinants responsible for specific intraits, as color differences, disease resistance, and size, to improve strength, rate of maturing, fertility, and other desirable traits. Devises means, such as use of chemicals, heat, and light, for altering or producing new traits.

10. *Marketing Specialist—Research.* Conducts research related to marketing conditions, often jointly with interested processors, wholesalers, and retailers. Observes and studies marketing methods and procedures in actual use. Uses acquired skills in marketing, business administration, economics, statistics, and related subjects in making comparisons of methods and procedures and arriving at solutions.

11. *Phytochemist.* Is concerned with such problems as the action of chlorophyll in photosynthesis; protein and fat synthesis in plants; the functions of minerals in plants; methods of increasing the content in plants of valuable components such as alkaloids or insecticidal principles; conditions affecting pigment production in fruits and vegetables (as the color of beets or apples); effects of various external treatments, as fertilizers, on the keeping qualities of fruits and vegetables in storage; study of the growth substances or plant hormones with a view toward practical applications, as in the rooting of cuttings and the production of seedless fruits; study of the internal chemical ratios that are correlated with vegetative growth, flowering, and fruiting; and study of the chemical aspects of immunity to disease in certain strains of crop plants.

12. *Plant Geneticist.* Seeks to discover and interpret various phenomena of the hereditary processes in plants, usually working with relatively few species and attempting to systematize and correlate his findings with cytological, morphological, and physiological situations. Utilizes mathematics as a basic tool in analyzing, interpreting, and forecasting the relative occurrence of parental and nonparental types from one generation to another.

13. *Ornamental Horticulturist.* Conducts experiments and investi-

gations on methods of improving quality and production of ornamental plants, such as flowering bulbs, herbaceous annuals and perennials, woody flower-bearing shrubs and trees, cacti, aquatic plants, and vines. Seeks such results as improved color or shape, increase in number of blooms, resistance to disease, and adaptability to conditions of shipping and storage. May be more specifically known as floriculturist, specialist in flower culture; arboriculturist, specialist in the culture, artistic planting, and trimming of trees and shrubs.

14. *Plant Breeder.* Plans and carries out breeding studies at experiment stations or farms to develop and improve varieties of field crops. Utilizes principles of genetics and knowledge of plant problems to achieve specific characteristics, such as improved yield, size, or quality; resistance to frost, drought, and disease. Determines varieties for crossing, and selects most representative plants of the variety. Utilizes various breeding methods, such as inbreeding, cross-breeding, back-crossing, out-crossing, and interspecific hybridization and detection. Plant breeding may be involved in the work of other classifications, such as agronomist, botanist, forester, or horticulturist.

15. *Pomology Research.* Conducts research in the science of fruit growing for a state experiment station, a university, or a chemical company. May make chemical, physical, or mechanical analyses of fruit plant tissues; conduct field trials of new varieties of fruits; experiment with new and old cultural practices to determine which are to be recommended to growers.

16. *Research Agricultural Engineer.* For an institution or an industrial firm, seeks to discover and solve new problems or new phases of old problems in the use of processing equipment; devises new methods of agricultural processing and recommends basic design for the necessary equipment.

17. *Soil Scientist.* Studies soil characteristics, identifies and maps soil types, and investigates responses of soils to known management practices to determine use capabilities of soil and effects of alternative practices on soil productivity; studies soil origin, distribution, and composition, and classifies soils according to standard types. Conducts experiments on farms or at an experiment station to determine soil tests best suited for different plants. Makes chemical analyses of soil management practices on the microorganism content of the soil. Investigates problems of stabilization and drainage of soils used as

foundations for roads, dams, buildings, and other structures. Advises on rural land use and management, and soil use on construction. May specialize in one or more of these activities.

18. *Wildlife Research Biologist.* Applies basic scientific principles to the study of the biology of game animals. Devises and develops methods of controlling populations of game animals and other wild animals. Studies the life history of important species; the plants utilized by game animals, their values, and frequently their utilization in food plots; parasites, diseases, and other decimating or controlling factors; exotic plant and animal species with possible game management values.

19. *Zoologist-Embryologist.* Studies the development of animals, including the formation of gametes, their union, and subsequent development of the embryo. Compares the embryonic development of various species. Studies genetic and environmental factors affecting development, as well as causes of embryonic abnormalities.

20. *Zoologist-Physiologist.* Studies the functions of various parts of animals, with special reference to chemical processes occurring and their relation to the activities of the animal as a whole. Measures muscle activity, nerve function, excretion, digestion, and blood composition. An endocrinologist specializes in the study of endocrine control of the body.

Chapter XI

Animal Industries

The animal industry is one of the largest industries in the United States. The production and marketing of livestock, poultry, and livestock and milk products will always be important, because it provides a food which is one of the basic needs of man. Meat, which is high in protein and energy value, also supplies vitamins, minerals, and essential fatty acids. The raising of farm animals dates back to the beginning of civilization itself. Animal domestication probably began in prehistoric times as a means of providing the food supply when hunting wild game was poor.

From very early times, the dog was domesticated for hunting, companionship, and protection by night. As man developed a more settled way of life, he began to plant seeds near his campsite; roots, bulbs, nuts, and grain were stored for winter use. Other animals were domesticated at about the same time to provide food, clothing, transportation, and power. Throughout the centuries, animals have remained a basic source of these necessities.

The animal industry in the United States has experienced a great change from the days of the Western cowboys, with their colorful personalities, manners, and customs.

In the early days, cattle roamed over millions of unfenced acres until ready for market, and it usually took two years to produce an animal of marketable size.

The present-day animal industry comprises a large number of businesses, including producers, suppliers, marketing specialists, packers, distributors, and other specialists, all endeavoring to supply the consumer with a high-quality food. The industry is changing and advancing to meet the needs of our changing diets. Today's family refrigerator might contain such animal products as beef, pork, lamb, poultry, milk, and many other by-products of the animal industry.

Production of a high-quality animal product requires well-managed farms for the growing of pasture, hay crops, grains, and by-products for feeding animals. These feeds are usually combined and used to produce animals for their meat, milk, eggs, wool, and other products. All of these areas of business require men to work in production, management, processing, marketing, storage, distribution, and health control.

The broad field of the animal industry is concerned with the production, feeding, management, breeding, and marketing of its products. It includes the following general areas of specialization:

Animal Science, or *Husbandry,* the science of selection, breeding, feeding, marketing, and management of beef cattle, hogs, horses, mules, sheep, and goats. Research in methods of grading and processing meat animals belongs in this area.

Dairy Science, or *Husbandry,* the science of selection, breeding, feeding, and management of dairy cattle and the production of milk.

Poultry Science, the science of production, management, feeding, breeding, selection, housing, and marketing of poultry—especially chickens, turkeys, ducks, and geese—and the sale of poultry products, chiefly eggs and meat.

ANIMAL SCIENCE

The field of animal science is concerned with the production, management, marketing, and processing of livestock. It further deals with supplying the food and fiber from animal products. It is a permanent, satisfying, and challenging work.

The animal scientist has many chances for specialization in the breeding, nutrition, and management of beef and dual-purpose cattle, horses and mules, pet animals, sheep, goats, and swine. He may work with animal products such as meats and their by-products or wool and other animal fibers, and do research in any of these phases.

Employment Opportunities

The animal scientist may acquire a general background and become an owner or manager of a farm or farms, combining any or all of the above-mentioned animals. In this position he may supervise a considerable force of men, including herdsmen and other farm workers.

The animal scientist may buy and sell livestock as a business, act for a livestock commission or brokerage concern, or purchase livestock for a commercial processor.

All breed associations have field representatives, secretaries, and office staffs. In this work the breed representative keeps records, visits and reports on livestock exhibits, coordinates activities of the association, and helps in publishing a periodical. Such a trained man may organize purebred livestock sales, tabulate pedigrees, prepare catalogues, and conduct auction sales.

Many agricultural magazines have livestock editors, and breed papers need men who can write. Insurance companies employ men to write policies, appraise, adjust claims, and make settlements for livestock insurance. Railroads need trained men as agents in obtaining livestock shipping business, acting as claim adjusters, and reducing traffic loss and injuries during shipment. Commercial feed companies employ animal nutritionists to plan and supervise preparation of formulas.

Specialists in the grading and classification of wool may be employed by a private or cooperative wool company. They may work as independent dealers or representatives of wool organizations. Leather experts find similar work that requires special knowledge of the handling, processing, and manufacture of leather.

Equipment dealers may want animal husbandmen to advise in the manufacture, sale, and installation of all types of equipment—haying tools, milking supplies, shearing machinery, and restraining devices for animals.

The animal scientist may teach in agricultural colleges at home or abroad; he may carry on research projects at colleges, experiment stations, market centers, and manufacturing establishments; he may join the extension staff of the state; or he may take a Civil Service position such as feed inspector.

Rapid growth of locker systems and home freezers has increased the need for men as processors and inspectors in the meat-packing industry.

The field of animal science is as broad or as narrow as one chooses to make it. Research possibilities are endless, as is the production side of the picture. There will always be a need for efficient, trained men in such an important industry.

Related Fields

Animal science is closely allied to many agricultural and biological sciences because of the broad scope of the required training. It is thus related to (1) poultry and dairy husbandry, in which the basic training is similar to that of animal husbandry; (2) veterinary science, especially in animal production, in which nutrition and management relate to health and disease prevention; (3) economic zoology, as a basic animal science; (4) agricultural and food chemistry and bacteriology, as these relate to animal nutrition, physiology, and products technology; (5) agricultural economics and agronomy, as related to marketing, management, and nutrition; (6) parasitology and medical entomology; and (7) genetics, as related to animal breeding.

Related nonprofessional fields are principally those which apply the findings of science in commercial enterprises. Among the important nonprofessional occupations which may be closely allied with the work of the professional animal husbandman are: (1) subordinate (subprofessional) workers in research activities, such as scientific aides, laboratory assistants, and agricultural aides; (2) routine inspectors and testers such as milk testers, meat graders, dairy inspectors, and cattle or livestock market inspectors; (3) commercial operators of fur farms, cattle ranches, and other animal farms, commercial animal breeders or fanciers, and herdsmen; and (4) salesmen, distributors, and processors of livestock or meat products.

Fields of Specialization

Breeding. The animal breeder attempts to produce strains of animals better adapted for efficient production and more suitable to the market than those previously available. The improvement sought may be increased milk production, more rapid growth and fattening, more efficient utilization of feed, better quality meat and wool, resistance to disease, or the development of new strains having better adaptation to certain climatic conditions. He is concerned with growth and development as related to particular characters where variation is only partly due to heredity, as contrasted with situations where characters are completely determined by hereditary traits.

The animal breeder is also concerned with the vigor of offspring resulting from the crossing of strains or races for market production; and with artificial insemination as a means of increasing the usefulness of superior sires or lowering the costs of sire service.

The animal breeder uses three basic methods to develop improved strains: (1) selection within existing breeds, using progeny testing and close breeding; (2) crossing of strains within breeds and crossing of breeds to obtain new combinations of desirable characters, through breeding and selection in the later generations; and (3) introduction of new strains from foreign countries and incorporation of their desirable traits into domestic breeds through crossing followed by selection.

While the principles of genetics and physiology utilized in animal breeding apply generally to all classes of livestock, many variations in techniques and procedures are necessary to meet the particular problems connected with the breeding of different classes of animals. The swine breeder, for instance, seeks productivity of sows, rate of gain, efficiency of feed utilization by pigs, and quality of meat cuts. He must therefore have a thorough knowledge of the fundamentals of related fields, including genetics, physiology, morphology, nutrition, and biometry.

Nutrition. Most animal husbandmen working in this field carry out controlled experiments to determine the feed requirements of various classes and ages of animals under varying conditions of work or production of the feeds; the materials that will furnish these requirements; the effect of deficiencies of one or more nutrients upon the animal organism; the digestibility of the nutrients of different feeds; the energy value of feeds; and the effect of storage and various processes and preparations on the nutritive value of feeds. They determine specifically the kind and quality of nutrients—such as proteins, carbohydrates, fats, fibers, minerals, vitamins, and water—required for increasing rates of production; the way in which chemical compounds of the feed are broken down into their component parts in the digestive tract and recombined to form the chemical compounds of the animal body; and the complex chemical reactions involved in these changes.

The extension worker in this field, by demonstration and education, carries the results of research to practical application by the farming public. Others specialize in teaching animal nutrition in colleges, universities, and vocational agricultural schools; or in consulting work wherein they advise on feeding problems for various classes of livestock.

The animal nutritionist requires a knowledge of fundamental chemistry, especially organic and biological, as well as anatomy, physiology, bacteriology, and statistics. He must be familiar with vitamin-deficiency symptoms and vitamin therapy, with mineral-deficiency symptoms and corrective treatment, and be able to cooperate with veterinary specialists and geneticists to distinguish nutritional deficiencies from symptoms brought about by infectious disease or heredity.

Animal Physiology. The animal physiologist is principally a researcher who through experiments adds to the existing knowledge of the functioning of various parts of the animal body and how these functions are affected by nutrition, management, and other factors. Such knowledge is used to increase the economic value of domestic animals. He determines the factors—such as nutrition, glandular secretions, temperature, light, or heredity—which control specific bodily activities such as lactation, fat deposition, rate of growth, and fertility.

The physiologist is trained in anatomy, histology, pathology, hygiene, chemistry, genetics, and microscopy. He uses his knowledge of anatomy in recognizing abnormal conditions of organs, tissues, or bones; of histology in recognizing changes or differences in tissues and their arrangement in organs; of pathology in distinguishing abnormalities due to disease from those due to heredity, nutrition, or some other factor; and of hygiene in understanding the conditions that favor the healthy functioning of the organs of the body. He uses his knowledge of physiology, chemistry, physics, genetics, and microscopy in identifying, measuring, and interpreting specific physiological activities.

Management (or Production). An animal scientist specializing in livestock management or production is usually employed in research, extension, marketing, or teaching, or in a combination of these. His interests often involve those of the breeder, veterinarian, geneticist, or nutritionist, since all of these sciences are important elements in livestock management.

By scientific experiments and field surveys, he carries out research into the nature, origin, handling, distribution, conservation, and improvement of the different classes of livestock. Other studies include functional requirements of housing, feeding, sanitation, parasite and disease control, and economic problems of supply and demand.

Extension work consists in the dissemination of the principles of livestock management through demonstration and education, including planning and supervision of demonstration projects with such organizations as the Grange, Farm Bureau, Farmers' Unions, Future Farmers Clubs, and 4-H Clubs, as well as directly with individual farmers. Some such experts specialize in teaching livestock management in colleges, universities, and vocational agricultural schools. Others do consulting work in an advisory capacity; write for technical journals; or work in statistical or economic capacities, setting up production goals and forecasting trends in supply, demand, and prices. The management expert also may specialize in livestock marketing, which deals with classification and grading of market livestock, methods and machinery of marketing, costs, and shipment of livestock. Livestock management requires a fundamental knowledge of such fields as genetics, nutrition, physiology, chemistry, zoology, bacteriology, statistics, agronomy, livestock judging, grading, and meat processing.

Animal Products Technology. The wool or animal-fiber technologist is concerned with the scientific and technical aspects of the production of wool and other animal fibers such as mohair, cashmere, camel's hair, llama, alpaca, vicuña, and rabbit hair.

He carries out scientific and technical studies of the nature, origin, use, and improvement of the fibers; the application of scientific principles to their growth on the respective animals; and the manufacturing methods required for converting the fibers into useful articles such as cloth, blankets, felts, rugs, carpets, pillows, mattresses, sleeping bags, upholstery, brushes, and various other specialties.

The technologist of wool and other animal fibers requires knowledge of animal science, physics, chemistry, engineering, and economics. Specialists in animal fiber technology often need to pursue the work of blending animal fibers with other materials, including plant fibers and synthetic fibers.

Such a technologist may specialize in one or more of the following functions: (1) research into the nature, origin, production, distribution, use, conservation, and improvement of wool and other animal fibers; (2) extension of the principles of technology through demonstration and education, including such work with producers, distributors, processors, and manufacturers of wool and other animal fibers; (3) teaching in colleges, universities, and technical schools; (4) consulting work on the growth and improvement of animal fibers and their classification, distribution, processing, manufacturing, and use;

and (5) management of production, distribution, processing, manufacture, and sales of wool and hair and the products made from them.

DAIRY SCIENCE

Dairy scientists and dairymen are engaged in one of the animal industry's largest areas—the production of milk. Agricultural income from dairy farming exceeds that of any other area of agricultural industry. Milk and other dairy products are among the foods most essential for good health. Dairy scientists may specialize in herd production, management, breeding, showing, or marketing.

Employment Opportunities

With college training dairy scientists may find many fields of interest and employment in teaching, administration, extension work, research, and sales. Examples include work with agricultural colleges and universities, feed manufacturers, dairy cattle associations, milk processors, breeding establishments, and the Federal government.

The man interested in scientific breeding, nutrition, milk production, and herd management can teach or carry out a research program in a university or an agricultural experiment station. He may prepare scientific reports and nontechnical bulletins detailing the results of experiments and the practical application of their findings. Dairy extension work is another challenging field, requiring men with specialized training to teach dairy farmers the more efficient methods of production, management, and marketing.

A specialist in the area of breeding is concerned with problems of herd improvement and breed efficiency. Herd improvement through selection, inbreeding, and line breeding is based on a thorough understanding of pedigree, hereditary factors, and breeding methods.

The dairy-farm owner must have a genuine liking for dairy cattle; the capital necessary to become established; and an understanding of the importance of accurate records and constant attention to the farm.

The dairyman may be interested in managing a herd of cattle owned by someone else, supervising the care, feeding, breeding, record-keeping, milk production, advertising, sales, and showing.

As a dairy-farm inspector he may be employed by the city, by a milk-processing plant, or a cooperative organization to make periodic inspection of dairy herds, equipment, and methods used on farms from which milk is purchased.

The dairy-science major may be employed by a feed manufacturer to sell dairy feeds, to help develop formulas, to work with experimental feeding projects, or to handle public relations.

Training

A student completing a four-year college course in dairy science will have no difficulty in finding a position to his liking. A degree is not essential for a private herdsman; but in the fields of research, education, and inspection a B.S. is necessary. Advanced degrees speed promotions, and the man with a degree will usually start at a higher salary. Farm experience is also essential.

Fields of Specialization

The dairy scientist carries out experimental investigations and demonstrates and teaches the application of scientific methods in the selection, breeding, nutrition, feeding, reproduction, lactation, and management of dairy cattle. He uses his knowledge of genetics, physiology, chemistry, nutrition, agronomy, anatomy, embryology, bacteriology, farm economics, and related branches of agricultural science in designing experiments or making field investigations, in analyzing data or results, and in arriving at conclusions and recommendations. He prepares scientific reports and nontechnical bulletins, setting forth the results of experiments and the practical application of his findings.

Some dairy scientists specialize in a particular technical activity, such as breeding or nutrition. Others specialize in a particular function, such as teaching, extension, or research, and do not ordinarily transfer from one to another, except that teaching and research are often combined.

The dairy management specialist is concerned with investigations or experimentation in the feeding and care of the milk cow; herd health; efficiency in production; handling of the herd sire; calf rearing; use of buildings and equipment; and advertising and selling livestock. He may also teach dairy management or carry out extension work in this field.

The specialist in dairy cattle breeding is concerned with various aspects of livestock improvement. The work of the teacher, extension specialist, or researcher in this area may deal with the physiology of reproduction, including conception, artificial insemination, gestation, parturition, and lactation; hygiene to control disease affecting reproduction; stock improvement techniques such as line-breeding, inbreeding, cross-breeding, and grading; the making of progeny tests and the proving of sires; and the role of genetics in improving the production of milk.

POULTRY SCIENCE

The poultry scientist engages in research, extension, teaching, or management work in relation to egg and poultry meat production. His work may deal with flock management; selection and breeding; effects of heredity and environment on hatchability; nutritional requirements of various types; improved methods of feeding, rearing, and housing; and disease prevention and control. He is interested in the economics of production, quality egg production and the marketing of poultry products.

Employment Opportunities

The poultry industry has grown from a backyard enterprise to a billion-dollar business, creating a large field for commercial production of eggs and meat.

The poultry scientist may own his own farm or hatchery or manage one for another. He may do testing and inspection work to insure compliance with local and state laws; he may advise or sell for a feed company; or he may grade poultry products sold on the market.

In addition to feeds and supplies, manufacturing, promotion, and servicing of equipment provide unlimited opportunities for the professional poultryman.

The poultry scientist with a master's or doctor's degree may advise in teaching, research, or extension work in colleges and experiment stations. He may supervise poultry improvement plans, preside at conventions; cooperate and exchange views with men from surrounding states; and secure, analyze, and interpret research data in terms of practical application. He may work in the area of disease control, development of new methods of production, selection, and culling of birds and new breeds.

In carrying out his work he makes use of his training in any of the following fields: anatomy, cytology, histology, genetics, nutrition, embryology, bacteriology, endocrinology, physiology, parasitology, pathology, physics, chemistry, statistics, or economics.

There are more opportunities available now than ever before in the commercial poultry business, and it seems sure that this trend will continue.

Fields of Specialization

The poultry breeding specialist makes use of the principles of genetics in breeding poultry for egg and meat production. His investigations involve the mode of inheritance of color and morphological and physical characteristics in the fowl. He is especially concerned with breeding problems relating to hatchability, egg size and shape, shell color, rate of growth, body shape and size, fleshing ability, plumage pattern, linkage, resistance to disease, early sexual maturity, rate of laying, and quality of eggs and meat. Principles involved in the selection of breeding stock and methods of mating employed in hatchery flocks are considered in their relation to improving the economic qualities of different classes of poultry.

The poultry nutrition specialist is concerned with the dietary requirements of poultry for energy, amino acids, minerals, and vitamins; with the feedstuffs which supply these factors; with the methods of feeding by which they are supplied; and with the metabolic processes to which they are subjected by the living organism. He also studies the deficiency diseases that develop when any of these elements are absent from the diet; and the effect of their presence in optimal or suboptimal quantities on growth, liveability, egg production, hatchability of eggs, and quality of eggs and poultry meat.

The poultry physiology specialist is concerned with the function of particular tissues or systems in poultry and with the functioning of the organism as a whole. He may investigate endocrine factors that control follicular growth and maturation, ovulation, and the development of the ovum; light as a factor in the regulation of ovulation and egg production; problems of fertility, hatchability, and development of the egg and embryo; semen production and fertilizing capacity of the male; and the physiological aspects of digestion and growth.

The poultry management specialist deals with methods of incubating, brooding, and rearing young stock for both meat production and layers, and methods of feeding and managing laying hens. He studies such factors as temperature and humidity requirements, litter requirements, forced moulting, battery brooding, and confinement and range management, all in relation to climatic conditions and the particular type of production desired. Adjustment of production to meet market requirements and the economic problems involved in poultry production, processing, and distribution may be included.

The poultry products specialist deals with factors affecting the quality of eggs and poultry meat; grades and grading of eggs and poultry; methods of preparing poultry and poultry products for market, including killing, dressing, and eviscerating poultry; the processing of frozen and dried eggs and poultry meat in various forms; marketing systems and methods of marketing eggs and poultry; and factors affecting the price and consumption of poultry products. He also studies the nutritive value of eggs and poultry meat and their relative importance in the human diet.

Job Descriptions in Animal Industries

1. *Anatomist.* Studies form and structure of animal bodies; examines large organs of body by systematic observation and dissection (gross histology). Compares the structures of species. Studies ability of animal bodies to regenerate destroyed or damaged parts and the possibility of transplanting organs and skin segments from one living body to another. Usually specializes in one of the functional systems of the body, such as respiratory, digestive, glandular, circulatory, or nervous systems.

2. *Animal Breeder.* Studies the influence of heredity and environment and their interaction on animal performance. Develops systems of mating and breeding. Determines the genetic composition of populations and heritability of traits. Utilizes principles of genetics and knowledge of animal-production problems to breed into economically important animals specific characteristics, such as improvement in strength, rate of maturing, disease resistance, or meat quality. Crosses animals within existing strains or crosses strains or breeds to obtain new combinations of desirable characteristics. If breeding is subordinate to other professional duties in a field of animal science, classification should be made as animal scientist, dairy scientist, or poultry scientist.

3. *Animal Ecologist.* Studies effects of various environmental influences on distribution, physical characteristics, behavior, and life

history of animals. Studies such environmental factors as plant growth, rainfall, temperature, altitude, and sunlight in relation to animal life. Scientists who study environmental relationships as an incidental function are classified according to major specialization, as aquatic biologist, herpetologist, ichthyologist, invertebrate zoologist, mammalogist, ornithologist.

4. *Animal Fiber Technologist.* Studies nature, origin, use, and improvement of wool and similar animal fibers, such as mohair, cashmere, camel's hair, and alpaca, as well as bristles and feathers; applies principles of animal husbandry to improving growth of fibers on animals. Develops improved manufacturing methods for converting fibers into commercial articles. Conducts experiments in blending animal fibers with others, including plant and synthetic fibers. May be designated according to specialty, as wool technologist.

5. *Animal Nutritionist.* Plans and conducts investigations in livestock nutrition. Determines composition of important feedstuffs, compiles rations, tests performance of animals on different rations, conducts grazing trials and metabolism studies. Determines the interrelationships among nutrients. Studies nutrient imbalances, deficiencies, and toxicities. Develops alternate systems of livestock production.

6. *Animal Pathologist.* Conducts basic research in the field of nutritionally created pathological conditions, including nutrient deficiencies, imbalances, and toxicities.

7. *Animal Scientist.* Usually specializes in one of the following fields: production, breeding, feeding, or physiology of reproduction of beef cattle, sheep, swine, and/or horses. May be a specialist in meats or in basic nutrition and biochemistry. Plans and conducts experiments in all phases of livestock production and reproduction to determine growth patterns, response to environment, and the influence of breeding, feeding, and management on the economics of production and the quality and quantity of product produced.

8. *Animal Taxonomist.* Studies animals for purposes of identification and classification. Scientists who practice taxonomy as an incidental function are classified according to their major specialization, as herpetologist.

9. *Apiculturist.* Devises and conducts experiments in pollination, causes and control of bee diseases, factors affecting yield of nectar and pollen of various plants utilized by bees, research on royal jelly,

vitamin content of various honeys, and selective breeding by artificial insemination to improve bee strains.

10. *Buyer, Livestock.* Purchases livestock from yards and growers for resale to packing houses and private individuals. Usually operates through livestock commission house, but may function independently.

11. *Entomologist.* Studies insects and their relation to plant and animal life. Identifies and classifies all species of insects and allied forms. Aids in control and elimination of pests by developing improved insecticides and biological methods, including use of birds, natural parasites, and other enemies that prey upon destructive insects. Develops means to encourage growth and spread of beneficial insects, including bees and those used as food by birds and fish. Studies insect distribution and habitat and recommends methods to prevent importation and spread of injurious types.

12. *Federal Coordinator (Poultry).* Utilizes advanced training in fields such as poultry genetics, diseases, or nutrition to coordinate Federal or regional programs, such as the National Poultry Improvement Plan and the Disease Eradication Program. Meets with industry representatives and research and extension workers to formulate and execute plans to implement Federally supported programs.

13. *Dairy Scientist.* Conducts research in selection, breeding, feeding, and management of dairy cattle. Studies feed requirements and nutritive value of feed materials. Carries out experiments to determine effects of feeds and environmental conditions on quantity, quality, and nutritive value of milk produced. Develops improved practices in care and management of dairy herds and use of improved buildings and equipment. Studies physiology of reproduction and lactation and carries out programs to improve dairy breeds (animal breeder). May be designated according to specialty, as dairy-management specialist, dairy-nutrition specialist.

14. *Hatcheryman.* Operates a hatchery for the production of chicks, poults, ducklings, and other domestic or game birds. Is responsible for the maintenance and operation of incubators; sanitation procedures; grading and handling of chicks; vaccinating and debeaking; and preparation for shipment.

15. *Herdsman.* Is responsible for care and management of livestock in large-scale commercial enterprises, and sometimes for fitting livestock for presentation at sales and shows. Requires knowledge of nutrition, genetics, physiology, and disease control. Should under-

stand production and marketing costs. On a private farm, should understand the growing of grain and roughages.

16. *Veterinarian (Doctor of Veterinary Medicine)*. Diagnoses diseases, disorders, and injuries of animals; treats animals medically or surgically. Tests dairy herds for tuberculosis and brucellosis; inoculates animals against diseases such as hog cholera and rabies. Performs autopsies to determine causes of death. Inspects animals intended for human consumption, before and after slaughtering. Advises on care and breeding of animals. May be engaged in general practice; or may restrict his practice to dogs, cats, and other pets, or to a single species, such as cattle, horses, or poultry. May engage in a particular function, such as research and development, consultation, administration, teaching, or technical writing and editing.

17. *Zoologist*. Studies all types of animals, including their origin, interrelationships, classification, life histories, habits, behavior, life processes, diseases, relation to environment, growth and development, genetics, and distribution. Makes field trips to study animals in natural habitat and collects specimens for laboratory study. Dissects and studies specimens under microscope; uses chemicals and various types of scientific equipment to carry out experimental studies. Prepares collections of preserved specimens or microscope slides for such purposes as identification of species, study of development, or study of animal diseases. May raise specimen animals for experimental purposes. May specialize in one aspect of animal study, such as the functioning of the animal as an organism (physiology), or development of the organism from the egg to embryo stage (embryology). Scientists who specialize in study of form and structure of animals are classified as anatomists or cytologists.

18. *Zoologist, Economic*. Is concerned with the control of destructive species of wildlife. Carries out control programs where wildlife species are causing economic damage.

Chapter XII

Business and Industry in Agriculture

One hundred years ago the United States was largely a nation of farmers. Three out of four families lived and worked on farms. Their activities were largely confined to producing food, clothing, and shelter. They purchased practically no supplies or equipment for use on the farm and had little need for agricultural businesses and industries as we know them today.

The shift during the last half century stems from new and improved methods of farming. The necessity for greater agricultural efficiency resulted in new machines, scientific methods of feeding, the use of fertilizer and pesticides, and improvement in crop varieties. These changes have all played an important role in the development of thousands of businesses to serve the dynamic commercial farmers of this country.

Decisions that lead to success in these businesses can usually be made best by people who have a working knowledge of farming, agriculture, and business.

As we see fewer and fewer farms and farmers, many of us conclude that agriculture is a declining industry. But farming today is only a part of the agricultural picture. Farmers have become more specialized in production; therefore, many of the facets of agribusiness—such as processing, transporting, retailing, and producing farm equipment—are being done by others who, in turn, specialize in these functions. Agribusiness is a growing industry, a vital force in a rapidly changing society.

Farmers used to sell products directly to consumers. But, imagine individual farmers trying to supply one of our large cities with food products today! The years have widened the distance from farm to consumer both in distance and service. The people who handle the in-between functions are called "middlemen." They, too, are part of agribusiness, which can be divided into five basic groups:

1. Farming.

2. Processing farm products.
3. Wholesaling farm products.
4. Retailing farm products.
5. Supplying farmers with production materials.

Farming creates more than three jobs off the farm for every job on the farm. The 7,000,000 farm workers who produce food and fiber exceed in number the combined employment in transportation, public utilities, and the steel and automobile industries.

At least 16,000,000 additional workers have jobs related to agriculture; 6,000,000 are employed in providing the supplies and equipment farmers use for production, and 10,000,000 others have jobs processing, storing, transporting, and selling the products of agriculture.

More than 60 per cent of the net worth of all United States businesses is in those dealing with agriculture, including farms and the firms that supply them and process, distribute, and market their products.

Agriculture is our nation's biggest producer of raw materials—the products that turn the wheels of industry. Feeding, clothing, and providing the products of better living for more than 185,000,000 people every day is our biggest business, even including national defense.

No other industry has increased its efficiency as rapidly as agriculture during the past few years, with the result that fewer workers are required in production while expanding numbers are needed each year supplying, servicing, and marketing agricultural production.

Business principles are increasingly important on the production side of agriculture as well as in marketing and processing. The demand for college-trained specialists who are experts in agriculture and understand business principles has far outrun the supply.

Business management is one of the largest fields of employment for young men with agricultural college degrees; it also offers numerous opportunities for those with less education. Thousands of salaried workers—85 per cent of them men—were employed in 1964 to manage the business activities of enterprises ranging from agricultural advertising to wood technology. In addition, many persons designated as professionals—such as scientists and accountants—also have administrative responsibilities. Some foremen and supervisors in processing plants or offices may perform functions that overlap managerial activities. There are also many proprietors who carry on all or a part of the activities necessary for the management of their own businesses.

The management setup varies widely among companies, depending on the size of the organization, the volume and type of agricultural business, and other factors. Regardless of such differences, most business firms hire young people as management- or business-trainees in order to insure an adequate supply of experienced personnel to fill vacancies as they occur at higher levels. Most large companies recognize two levels of management position above that of supervisor and manager-trainee—the middle management group and the top-level management officials. In the biggest companies, a typical managerial setup includes a president, several vice presidents—each in charge of one or more broad functions, such as production, marketing and sales, or finance—and several middle or department managers who report to the vice president in charge of their area of work.

Success stories about corporation presidents who quit school and started work as messengers or office boys in their firms appear now and then in magazines and books. Such stories make fascinating reading and lead boys and girls to dream of similar accomplishments. However, young people should know that the "self-made" man is becoming a rarity. It is increasingly difficult for the person without a broad educational background to move up through the ranks of a company to a top management position.

For meaningful career planning, young people interested in management positions need to know as much as possible about the nature of the work to be performed and the training required. They should be acquainted with the types of management positions, with emphasis on the kinds of jobs open to new entrants; the educational and other qualifications required for entry; the ladders of advancement; future employment prospects; earnings; and other aspects of administrative work in private industry.

Management Career Areas[1]

Sales Department. Numerous opportunities for advancement to managerial positions are available in the sales departments of manufacturing companies, wholesale or retail stores, insurance companies, or almost any type of large business concern. Promotion usually depends upon a successful sales record. Employees who are college graduates are likely to advance more rapidly than those with less edu-

[1] From "Careers in Management," U.S. Department of Labor.

cation; however, sales work is an area in which it is still possible for persons with little or no formal education beyond high school to move up the promotion ladder if they have exceptional selling ability.

Production Department. Management personnel in the production department of manufacturing firms are responsible for seeing that products are turned out rapidly at the lowest possible cost consistent with maintaining quality. The virtually endless list of products includes those used by agricultural businesses that process and manufacture machinery, supplies, chemicals, motors and others—and consumer products ranging from canned goods to water pumps. The chief functions of the production department are production control—the scheduling of operations to insure that orders are turned out on time— and quality control—setting up of inspection and testing procedures to insure that goods meet established standards.

Research Department. Nearly every large manufacturing company has a department of research and development which is concerned with projects such as developing new products or improving methods of production. Some research projects may also be designed primarily to extend scientific knowledge. Such basic research often has practical value later; for example, knowledge of the chemical effects of radiation is being used to develop new methods of sterilizing food. A substantial amount of research carried on by private firms, in such fields as food processing, electronics, and new foods, is related to the nation's food supply.

Personnel and Industrial Relations Department. Workers in the personnel department help to employ and maintain an efficient work force for all departments in a business firm. This function includes a wide variety of jobs in which personnel workers interview, test, place, and counsel job applicants and employees. Personnel workers may also do work related to wage and salary administration, employee benefit plans, and employee communications, safety, and health.

Other Departments. Some companies have several separate departments in addition to those described above. In many cases, the top executives in overall charge of broad functions are responsible also for related departments; for example, the vice president in charge of production or manufacturing may be responsible for the purchasing and transportation departments, and the top executive in charge of marketing and sales may give general direction to the advertising department.

Opportunities

Over 50 per cent of the graduates of Colleges of Agriculture in the United States enter some form of business.

Training for agricultural business is broad enough to prepare for farm management, employment in marketing organizations, grain elevators, packing plants, storage houses, canneries, stockyards, terminals, buying stations, commodity exchanges, banks, and other credit agencies.

Marketing Steps. The marketing of agricultural products requires many steps from the farm to the consumer. The jobs of financing, insuring, buying, selling, storing, and distributing are all necessary and require trained personnel. The companies that process feeds, fertilizers, milk, and other products related to agriculture have many openings for young men with agricultural college training. The processing and distribution of milk is one of the largest industries at the present time.

Food Distribution. Food distributors are always seeking outstanding college graduates to train for purchasing, store management, and various commodity positions in their organizations. Representatives of these companies visit the college campuses each year to select top graduates. They are interested in a student's social activities, leadership, and personality as well as his scholastic record.

The areas of marketing poultry, eggs, beef, pork, vegetables, fruits, and other agricultural commodities offer many opportunities for the college graduate. The manufacturing and distribution of farm equipment, supplies, and feed require young men with training in agriculture, the biological sciences, economics, and other basic sciences.

Grain Elevator Employment. The grain elevator manager is responsible for a large variety of activities and decisions. He buys grain from farmers, usually on a grade basis; shells, processes, blends, and stores grain crops; and sells grain in carload quantities to millers, terminal elevators, and feed manufacturers. The manager also purchases and sells such farm supplies as feeds, fertilizers, seeds, fencing, and chemicals.

Training

The student interested in agricultural business needs a broad general educational background, regardless of the area of specialization he chooses. Opportunity is provided by the agricultural colleges for the student to give major emphasis to the business management and social problems of today's agricultural industries, rural people, and government. Because economic and social problems are involved in all segments of the agricultural production, supply, and distribution businesses, students may major in any of the following areas:

1. *Agricultural Business.* Students prepare for management and administrative positions, public relations, and sales positions with feed, fertilizer, chemical, machinery, and other industries supplying products and services used by farmers as well as the many industries engaged in marketing and distribution of agricultural products.

2. *Agricultural Credit and Finance.* Preparation is for management positions and for employment as farm loan specialists with farm credit agencies, commercial banks, insurance companies, and government agencies.

3. *Agricultural Marketing.* Study is for management positions with businesses engaged in marketing of farm products. Included are businesses which assemble, store, sell, finance, assume risk, disseminate market news, and process farm products.

4. *Food Merchandising.* Students prepare for management, personnel, sales, and buying positions with food wholesaling and retailing businesses.

5. *Foreign Agricultural Development.* Courses in this specialty, which includes both the economic and the social aspects of development, qualify students for employment in foreign countries. Government, business, and voluntary agencies furnish employment in this area.

6. *General Agricultural Economics.* Graduates in this area are prepared for graduate study and for work in agricultural extension, government positions, and other positions requiring a broad agricultural background. Some students specialize within this broad area and become agricultural statisticians, price analysts, agricultural policy specialists, land economists, or specialists in other areas of work.

Job Descriptions in Business and Industry

1. *Administrator, Agricultural.* Administers the affairs of an organization created to serve some phase of agriculture. Is responsible for the execution of policies and procedures to achieve stated objectives of the organization.

2. *Agricultural Agent.* Analyzes the agricultural problems of the

area served and works with interested individuals and organizations to promote changes that will benefit farmers and his employer. Assists in locating shipping and processing plants; studies the movement of materials to and from farms; cooperates with agencies such as the Agricultural Extension Service, the Farm Bureau, and others; attends meetings of agricultural organizations; keeps himself and his company informed concerning possible trends in agriculture; prepares exhibits and advertising material that may benefit farmers.

3. *Agricultural Co-Op Manager.* Assumes responsibility for the management of an organization which buys and sells cooperatively. Is employed by a board of directors to supervise and direct employees in the business. The scope of work, duties, and responsibilities vary widely among cooperatives, for they may deal in a single item—such as gasoline, wool, livestock, or fruits and vegetables—or a combination of items.

4. *Agricultural Representative.* Represents a large concern (railroad, packing plant, cement manufacturer) with a view toward building goodwill and maintaining contacts with farmers; a public relations, not a selling, job.

5. *Agricultural Statistical Analyst.* Collects, compiles, and interprets statistical data relating to production, marketing, and other phases of agriculture. May be employed by the Federal or state government or by private concerns having contacts with agriculture. Requires training in general agriculture, agricultural economics, and statistics.

6. *Agricultural Buildings Engineer.* Applies basic engineering science to the utilization of structures on the farm and in rural areas. Is responsible for selection of building materials, site, design, construction details, and utilization of the farm structure. May serve as consultant to manufacturing concerns or as rural building inspector for money-lending agencies.

7. *Agricultural Control Chemist.* Performs chemical analyses on macro- or micro-amounts of agricultural chemicals such as pesticides, plant-growth regulators, food additives. Develops specific methods to detect trace amounts of chemicals which may be present in crops at the time of harvest. Investigates the action of pesticides and plant-growth regulators, including enzyme action and inhibition. Studies the metabolic fate of agricultural chemicals in plants and animals as well as cell-free systems.

8. *Agricultural Consultant.* Consults with and advises individuals, organizations, or companies on agricultural matters in his specialty, such as agronomy, agricultural engineering, or soil conservation.

9. *Agricultural Marketing Specialist.* Operates as the link that joins the wants and needs of consumers with the productive facilities of farmers; helps the farmer market high-quality products more efficiently.

10. *Agricultural Implement Dealer.* Utilizes agricultural engineering training in the sale and servicing of farm machinery such as tractors, seeding equipment, harvesting machinery, farm supplies, and tools. Duties and responsibilities vary widely in different communities. Requires knowledge of agricultural problems and farm experience.

11. *Broker—Real Estate and Farm Land.* Appraises land, buildings, and other improvements for purpose of sale, purchase, or securing loans. May sell insurance and offer other services. May conduct a private enterprise or work as a part of the cooperative movement. Requires a complete knowledge of the agricultural industry.

12. *Broker—Buyer; Dealer.* Purchases and collects any kind of resalable goods, usually from individuals and for his own account, and resells to wholesalers or to private individuals; inspects and grades or appraises goods offered for sale, or in hope of inducing owner to sell, at owner's home or place of business. Sorts, grades, or otherwise classifies purchased articles for resale, but seldom processes them. Solicits purchasers for goods he has bought. Usually does not act as an agent for others.

13. *Broker—Food.* Acts as an agent; arranges contracts for buyers and sellers of food items. Facilitates business transactions but does not own or provide facilities for handling food items physically. May handle one or many accounts; may specialize in one particular item.

14. *Buyer—Grain.* Grain-elevator agent or employee. Manages a grain elevator, usually for a cooperative concern or a company. Examines samples of the load to ascertain the presence and extent of such price-affecting factors as moisture, dirt, burrs, hulls, seeds, and other dockage, and calculates the market value, either buying grain outright or issuing storage certificates. Keeps detailed daily records; supervises subordinates who dump the grain into a pit, grind and mix feeds to be sold, and prepare freight cars for loading. In smaller establishments, may personally perform these duties.

15. *Farm Credit Secretary.* Serves as secretary of a local farm-loan

association or a production credit unit of the Farm Credit Administration. Appraises applications for agricultural loans, approving, supervising, and collecting the loans. May perform similar functions with private banks.

16. *Fertilizer Salesman.* Utilizes knowledge of agronomy as an employee of a fertilizer company or cooperative organization; devotes the major part of his time to the sale of fertilizer for field crops, gardens, and lawns. May conduct field tests cooperatively with farmers, investigate complaints, and write reports and publish material on the values of fertilizer.

17. *Fertilizer Sales Representative.* Conducts educational work concerned with proper fertilizer usage. Contacts fertilizer dealers, farmers, and others to discuss research results obtained from experiment station work. May conduct fertilizer demonstrations with farmers. Primarily a contact man.

18. *Florist Broker—Salesman.* Acts as a grower's representative to the florist trade channels; keeps close contact with markets within shipping range in order to supply the less congested and the best open markets. Has as a primary function the getting together of flower buyers and sellers; does not take title to goods, nor does he physically handle the items.

19. *Florist Commission House Manager.* Maintains contact with growers of greenhouse crops and manufacturers of florist supplies and determines the quality and quantity of materials to be handled. Is responsible for supervision of distribution.

20. *Farm Produce Buyer.* Buys farm products wholesale, representing a broker, processor, exporter, or retail outlet. Is employed by a packer, chain store, processing plant, or other large buyer of farm products. Requires an intimate knowledge of the commodity handled as well as training in marketing.

21. *Farm Produce Salesman.* Assembles and sells farm products such as livestock, milk, eggs, fruit and vegetables, or others. May be employed by a cooperative organization or a private commission company. Requires training in marketing and business practices as well as a basic knowledge of the commodity handled.

22. *Farmers Home Administration Supervisor.* Directs the activities of an F.H.A. office in a designated area.

23. *Farm Appraiser.* Appraises or places a value on farm real estate and chattel property as the basis for a loan, a sale of the prop-

erty, or a purchase; or for taxation or the settlement of estates. Requires a knowledge of the agricultural industry.

24. *Foreign Service Representative (Agriculture).* Represents the United States government or a private concern with holdings or markets in a foreign country. Works on problems such as the prospects for exporting and importing agricultural products for the U.S. Department of Agriculture or the Department of State. Should know the language and customs of the foreign country and be willing to remain there for three years.

25. *Horticulturist (Garden Store Operator).* Requires training in horticulture, with thorough knowledge of vegetables and fruits, their planting and growth, harvesting methods, and marketing processes; ornamental flowers, shrubs, and lawn grasses; the basic principles of landscape design; and the annual care of such plants. Other essentials include business and management ability, experience in merchandising, personnel relations, and meeting the public; knowledge of accounting and bookkeeping.

26. *Manager of Agricultural Business.* With a background of two or more years as a teacher of vocational agriculture, manages a dairy herd, farm, greenhouse, nursery, chick hatchery, or community hardware or machinery store.

27. *Manager, Retail Hardware and Farm Implements.* Directs the operation of a retail trade devoted to selling hardware or farm implements; makes reports, takes and verifies inventories, purchases or requisitions goods, handles receipts, plans work and promotes sales.

28. *Manufacturer of Liming Materials.* Owns or operates a limestone-pulverizing plant producing liming materials for use on the land or hydrated lime. Agricultural liming materials are usually a byproduct of the manufacture of other limestone products.

29. *Retailer (Farm Products and Supplies).* Operates a food store or a dairy or produce department in a large store or market; may operate a farm supply store, selling farm machinery, feed, and fertilizer.

Chapter XIII

Communications and Public Relations in Agriculture

Interesting and dynamic careers in communications and public relations await the college graduate with training in agriculture combined with skill in writing, speaking, or illustrating.

It is fascinating work, this business of communicating with people. Farm journals, industrial publications, service magazines, informational leaflets, weekly and daily newspapers, and radio and television render important service to farmers, processors, food distributors, and consumers.

Men with a sound knowledge of agriculture combined with the ability to write or speak are in demand. There is a persistent demand for capable young men trained in both agriculture and journalism. The entire field of communications is receiving more and more emphasis. Successful business, regardless of the product being sold, is based upon the ability to communicate with the public.

Opportunities

The employment opportunities in the field of agricultural journalism are far more numerous than the supply of trained young men and women. College graduates may find careers in publicity, public relations, advertising, sales promotion, informational services of Federal and state governments, extension service, radio, television, and teaching.

Thousands of newspapers, popular magazines, trade journals, house organs, and agricultural publications need articles for their readers. Many of these articles are being written by agricultural college graduates.

The following areas are open to talented, trained persons, interested

110

in helping mankind through written, spoken, or visual communication:

1. *Agricultural Journalism.* There are approximately 1,500 daily and 8,000 weekly newspapers published in the United States, with the majority in agricultural areas and communities. Several hundred agricultural publications and trade journals include information regarding the several areas of agriculture.

2. *Radio.* Many radio stations across the country employ agriculturally trained persons to fill jobs as reporters, directors, and broadcasters.

3. *Television.* A hundred million people may be reached simultaneously over thousands of television stations. Television is one of the greatest educational media of the modern world. Young men and women with training in agriculture are filling many positions in this area.

4. *Audio-visual Education.* The use of television is creating a great need for all kinds of audio-visual aids and materials. Well-trained people in these new fields are continuously in demand, and this need will continue into the future.

5. *Public Relations and Promotion.* We are living in the age of automation, jets, rockets, and space travel. Yet the age of oxen and the wooden plow prevails in many countries within a day's travel from our homes.

The new world is taking shape in the physical, biological, and social sciences; it is possible to communicate in a matter of seconds with leading cities in every country of the world, yet there remains an atmosphere of distrust, concern, and lack of understanding.

The world population is growing so rapidly as to create additional food problems in many countries. The political, social, and economic aspects of the future will need strong programs of public relations and communication to solve world problems. A great future lies ahead for young men and women interested in winning friends and constructively influencing people.

There are many public-relations opportunities with trade associations, processors, manufacturers, distributors, implement companies, food industries, and practically any organization with a product to sell. The person in public relations needs good training along with high standards of moral ethics to succeed.

Training

The colleges of agriculture in each state can assist young men and women in choosing the best program for a career in agricultural communications.

The major requirements for such a career are the insight to recognize the problem and the ability to communicate with people. A high-school student who is interested in journalism should plan his program accordingly. High-school training in vocational agriculture provides an excellent foundation in the technical knowledge necessary to be a successful writer or public relations man in the field. Working on the high-school paper, writing news for the community paper, and getting summer jobs in some form of communications make good background for college training in agricultural communications.

College preparation for a career in agricultural journalism should include courses in animal and plant sciences, economics, and business organization as well as in journalism. Most agricultural colleges have working relationships with schools and departments of journalism for the training of agricultural students.

Chapter XIV

Conservation of Natural Resources and Rural Recreation

Conservation is a way of management and use of natural resources. As populations increase throughout the world, there is increasing need for conservation measures. In the United States the conservation programs of governmental agencies alone entail the annual expenditure of several billion dollars. Thousands of persons with general or specialized training in resource management are employed by private and public agencies. Both government and business leaders increasingly look to colleges and universities for persons with training in this field.

The field of conservation is so new that the nation's educational system has not yet had time to organize the necessary combination of training. Certain specialized areas such as forestry are exceptions. The person desiring to work in conservation should have a working knowledge of agronomy, biology, engineering, forestry, earth and soil science, ecology, range management, and other areas. At present, experience sometimes has to be substituted for formal college training in at least some of the fields.

Present curricula are designed for students who want to teach or do research, planning, regulatory, or management work in various phases of conservation. They provide a broad training in basic sciences, a general training in important areas of conservation, and an opportunity to specialize in one or more fields of conservation—soil, water, plant and animal life, and forest resources.

Many conservation programs are still relatively new. There will probably be spurts and lags in employment; but a slow, steady increase may be expected as more states put conservation on a sound, nonpolitical basis. A well-trained biologist should be able to fit into a wide range of employment opportunities.

Entry into the conservation field requires four years of college work; for research, teaching, and responsible positions, five years or more are preferred. Graduates with M.S. or Ph.D. degrees in agronomy, biology, or conservation will find excellent opportunities for employment in teaching, research, and extension work. State conservation departments ᴂmploy biologists, game managers, and fish management agents to assist in their wildlife programs. Other agencies offering employment in conservation include such Federal agencies as the Soil Conservation Service, the Forest Service, and the National Park Service. Teaching, extension work, research stations, writing, and similar fields offer opportunities.

Agronomy

Agronomy is the application of plant, soil, and related sciences to the improvement, production, and use of field crops. Yields of crops can be increased substantially by the use of better varieties and by improved practices of crop production, which is the backbone of successful farming. Training in agronomy is useful on the farm, or it may prepare you for a career in private or public service. Agronomists are employed in the following fields:

1. *Management.* There are opportunities for agronomists as managers of private farms or as field men for farm management service companies, canners, seedsmen, and other industries.

2. *Agricultural Extension.* Extension departments are maintained by both public and private institutions. An agronomist is qualified for a position as a county agent, 4-H Club agent, crop specialist, or soil conservationist. Railroads, mills, elevator companies, farm implement companies, and seed firms also frequently employ agronomists in their service departments.

3. *Regulatory.* Training in agronomy fits you for positions in the enforcement of state or Federal weed and seed laws. Agronomists are employed as seed-certification officials and in state and Federal grain inspection departments.

4. *Research.* State experiment stations, the U.S. Department of Agriculture, seed firms, canning companies, and sugar factories are among those who employ agronomists in the development and testing of new crop varieties. Research in production problems is carried on by farm implement companies, fertilizer manufacturers, and agricultural chemical companies making pesticides. Millers, crushers, and other processors continually study the problems of crop use.

5. *Sales*. There is a great demand for trained agronomists in sales and distribution of fertilizers, seeds, insecticides, fungicides, herbicides, and feeds.

6. *Miscellaneous*. Land appraisal, insurance adjustment, crop estimating, and agricultural journalism are possibilities for those whose interests and supplementary training fit them for such work.

Soil Conservation

The Soil Conservation Service, a Federal agency, furnishes practical assistance to farmers all over the country, urging soil conservation to increase crop yield. To serve as a technician administering this aid, a degree in conservation or its equivalent training and experience is desired. The S.C.S. also has its own training program under which recruits participate in a 6-week to 10-week intensive course of in-service training.

Soil conservationists are trained to provide technical assistance in planning, applying, and maintaining soil and water conservation improvement practices on farms, recreational areas, and watersheds. Farmers apply this assistance by adjusting their land-use practices; protecting land against soil deterioration; rebuilding eroded soils; reducing runoff; improving cover on crop, forest, pasture, range, and wildlife areas; and conserving water by constructing ponds or lakes and improving methods of drainage and irrigation.

Most soil conservationists are employed by the Federal government. Some work for colleges, banks, public utilities, and private agencies.

Fish and Wildlife Management

One of the most important recreational industries and the commercial fishing industry are based upon the proper use and harvesting of fish and game. These industries have passed the stage of depending upon the animals naturally present and are relying more and more upon the art of making the land produce sustained annual crops of fish and game. This production requires sound application of many branches of science in the light of economics, social forces, and informational programs. There are satisfying careers waiting for men trained in this field.

The opportunities in fish and wildlife management, research, and conservation education lie primarily in Federal and state agencies. Only a few opportunities are available for private employment. There is a steady demand for well-trained men. The continuing increase of interest in fishing and hunting and the ever-shrinking areas available to produce fish and game make it necessary to have more men to help provide technical information in several sciences.

The following broad categories illustrate a wildlife manager's work. Actually he will probably work within limited areas of the field, such as research or management of fish, waterfowl, big game, or commercial fisheries.

1. *Management.* Surveys of populations and regulation of the annual harvest of fish or game are needed.

2. *Research.* The habits and habitats of various kinds of fish or game are studied in order to devise methods for developing desirable populations of these animals.

3. *Education.* Not only must wildlife technicians be trained for their jobs, but sportsmen, landowners, and others must be made aware of the problems involved in the management of fish and game and how these problems may be solved.

4. *Refuge Management.* Refuges are set up for specific purposes, such as to furnish breeding areas for waterfowl. These require special types of intensive management.

5. *Habitat Development.* Many state departments are carrying out extensive programs to improve farm-game, trout-stream, and forest-game habitats on private lands. Here biologists work with landowners, Federal agencies, sportsmen's clubs, and other interested groups.

6. *Protection.* Law enforcement is a problem of education as well as police action. There is more and more demand for trained biologists to enter this field.

A fish management specialist is a graduate in conservation; he studies the requirements of fish and development of fish resources. He may be in charge of programs to stock ponds, lakes, and streams; he may work to control aquatic vegetation and determine correct restrictions on the harvesting of fish. Other duties include making surveys of fish resources, studying pollution problems and the condition of streams and lakes, and putting into effect a program of maximum fish production.

The biologist or wildlife technician may conduct surveys of wildlife resources; develop management plans for wildlife production on public and private land; carry on experiments and plan programs for control of injurious animals; superintend the wildlife program in public parks; manage farms for propagation of game animals and birds; and develop fur farms.

Forestry

Forestry deals, first of all, with the growing of continuous crops of trees on suitable lands. But the forester is also concerned with other values. He usually manages large areas of wildlands, regulating them in a manner to protect water supplies, furnish recreation, and produce wildlife and perhaps some forage for domestic livestock. Consequently, in addition to harvesting the crop of trees, the forester may find himself engaged in manufacturing, selling, public education, engineering, research, building, developing new processes of products, and law enforcement. Much of his work is with people; training them and supervising their work, enforcing laws and regulations, transacting business with them, and trying to gain their support for needed action.

The employment of foresters is about evenly divided between public and private agencies, with an increasing number going into business for themselves as consultants, as wood producers, as processors, or as forest landowners. The largest public employer of foresters is the United States Forest Service, which manages the national forests and employs the men known as Forest Rangers. Among other Federal agencies that employ foresters are the National Park Service, the Bureau of Land Management, the Office of Indian Affairs, the Tennessee Valley Authority, and the Fish and Wildlife Service. Most of the states have forestry departments, which protect state and privately owned forest lands from fire, manage state forests, grow and distribute planting stock for reforestation purposes, employ service foresters to work with the owners of forest lands, and enforce regulatory and protective laws. Foresters may also find public employment in state park systems, as county or city foresters, or in the teaching profession.

Over the past decade increasing numbers of foresters have been employed by industry. Most of them are engaged in growing the tree crops needed by the lumber or pulpwood industry, but others find employment in logging, manufacturing, and sales. They may also work in the field of product development or a wide variety of research activities.

Many people think that the forester lives in a remote cabin in the woods. It is true that there are still a few rather isolated ranger stations, but since so much of a forester's work concerns people, the forester is now usually stationed in the largest community adjacent to his work. Improved transportation facilities and public services have reduced much of the isolation experienced by foresters in the earlier days.

Training

Undergraduate Programs. Most students planning a career in some phase of the science of conservation will seek a bachelor of science degree from a college of agriculture. In general, programs leading to such a degree will include (1) courses required of all students in the college; (2) the minimum of basic courses required by the curriculum; (3) the courses required for the student's specialization by the major department; and (4) elective courses to bring the total number of credits to the required minimum.

Students whose primary interest does not fall within the sphere of some department in the college of agriculture may be able to arrange a suitable program in some other college.

Graduate Programs. Graduate work leading to the M.S., M.A., and Ph.D. degrees with specialization in some phase of resource conservation is available in many universities. Many graduate schools also permit students to pursue interdepartmental programs leading to graduate degrees. Through this arrangement, a graduate student already trained in a specialty can add to his knowledge in that field and broaden his training by including study in related areas. This type of preparation is especially important to the person interested in teaching, research, planning, or administration.

Students interested in doing graduate work should consult the bulletin of the graduate school for entrance requirements and details concerning registration. It is advisable for the graduate student to inquire further into the opportunities in his area of interest. This may be done by writing directly to the appropriate department in the college or university in your state.

Job Descriptions in Conservation and Recreation

1. *Agrogeologist.* Applies geological relations to agriculture, including land forms, soils and their origin, water supply, and mineral resources such as fertilizing materials (limestone, gypsum, sulphur, etc.). Employed by various Federal agencies.

2. *Agronomist.* Works with the physical, chemical, and biological situations, processes, and responses in soils and field crops, and with the organization of scientific systems of soil management and crop production. Because the field is so broad, agronomists tend to specialize either in the soil or the crop phases.

3. *Agricultural Consultant.* Consults with and advises individuals, organizations, or companies in a particular field in which he specializes, such as soil management, crop production, machinery requirements, and organization of farming systems.

4. *Agrostologist.* Specializes in grasses, usually in the identification, classification, morphology, and botanical phases other than plant breeding.

5. *Botanist.* Makes specific study of plants in field, in laboratory, or in both. May also teach plant science.

6. *Biologist.* Studies structures, processes, classification, and life histories of plants or animals. Originally studied both plants and animals, but plant and animal sciences now are customarily divided into botany and zoology.

7. *Conservationist.* Carries out programs sponsored by state agricultural experiment stations, state departments of conservation, and various Federal and commercial agencies for the preservation of natural resources such as soils, water, minerals, and wildlife.

8. *Erosion Specialist.* Concerns himself with the control of soil erosion by vegetative and engineering measures on crop land, pasture land, and in forested areas.

9. *Farm Planner.* Plans organization of farms to promote most effective program of conservation of soil and efficient farm management. Starts as an assistant farm planner in soil conservation district.

10. *Fish Management Specialist.* Conducts research and applies results to problems of producing good supply of edible fish in natural ponds, lakes, and streams.

11. *Forester.* Manages woodlots or other forest tracts, or city tracts and parks. May specialize in wildlife conservation as well as care, handling, and marketing of timber. May be employed by government, state, city, or private enterprise.

12. *Game Management Specialist.* Conducts research and applies results in fields of diseases, food, and cover requirements for wild animals; fur production; and vermin control.

13. *Herpetologist.* Conducts study into phases of reptile life; may care for reptile collection in a zoo.

14. *Ichthyologist.* Studies fish, their structure and habits; conducts research into methods of capturing, classifying, breeding, and distributing fish.

15. *Marine Biologist.* Is concerned with the economic importance of marine organisms, looking toward the prevention of damage to ships, pilings, wharves, and other structures, as well as toward the usefulness of seaweeds, shellfish, and fish resources.

16. *Museum Curator.* Administers a museum and conducts research into history of exhibits.

17. *Naturalist.* Makes special study of animals or plants. Specifically designated as botanist or zoologist.

18. *Nature-Study Counselor.* Teaches courses on bird, plant, and animal life to young people in camps, settlement houses, or other organizations engaged in group work.

19. *Ornithologist.* Conducts study in phases of bird life; conducts research into their structure, identification, habitat, migration, and diet.

20. *Outdoor-Life Writer.* Writes articles for newspapers and magazines on topics related to nature and outdoor living.

21. *Park Superintendent.* Supervises public use of city, state, and national parks and parkways; maintains park buildings and grounds; directs movement of traffic and parking of automobiles; registers campers; furnishes information on rules and regulations of parks; keeps camps and parks in sanitary and attractive condition; directs landscape planting and maintenance; and supervises recreational facilities.

22. *Range Conservationist.* Helps to conserve and improve the resources of the nation's range lands, which comprise almost a billion acres, produce more than half of the nation's livestock, and support more than one-fifth of all the rural families in the country. Must know the soils of the range country; its important plants, their value, when they grow, how they reproduce, and how closely they may be grazed with safety to future forage crops and protection against erosion; the grazing habits of livestock, their nutritional requirements, and the various methods of livestock management. Must be able to make and read maps.

23. *Soil Conservationist.* As an agronomist, directs the state con-

servation district. Visits farms and investigates and develops plans for soil, water, forest, wildlife, and vegetation control and crop rotation; works with local, Federal, and state organizations; supervises building of terraces and ponds.

24. *Soil Management Specialist.* Applies principles of nature and properties of soils to derive better systems of soil management. Employed by governmental agencies to advise and direct the public in management and conservation practices; or work in a managerial capacity on a large farm.

25. *Soil Mapper.* Prepares maps showing distribution of soil types. May be associated with the Soil Survey or an organization requiring information concerning soil distribution.

26. *Soil Physicist.* Investigates problems in soil deterioration, improvement, and management; tillage; irrigation; drainage; and soil-plant relationships. May work with and advise conservationists and producers of tillage implements, as well as construction engineers concerned with foundation structures.

27. *Soil Scientist.* Conducts research in all phases of soil and soil management in universities or government agencies. Teaches, directs work of others interested in soil science.

28. *Soil Specialist.* As an agronomist, devotes his knowledge and services to the solution of problems relating to the management, conservation, and improvement of soil.

29. *Soil Surveyor.* Identifies and classifies soils; prepares maps showing soil distribution and other physical land features. Employed by state experiment stations and Federal agencies including the Soil Survey and the Soil Conservation Service.

30. *Specialist in Soil Drainage.* Aids in planning and directing drainage projects by Federal or state agencies, or by individuals or groups. Works with foresters, agronomists, and power and machinery engineers to construct and maintain suitable devices, machinery, and methods of tillage to remove excess water and conserve soil and water.

31. *Wildlife Collector.* Advises on, administers, supervises, or performs research or other scientific work in the classification of animals. Work involves the review of existing systems of classification; the collection of specimens of animals; studies of their ecology, structure, function, distribution, habits, life history, and economic importance; and preservation or exhibition of specimens or collections.

32. *Wildlife Manager.* Makes ecological studies of birds or mammals in their natural environment; conducts studies directed toward the preparation of management plans for game species, or for the wildlife of an area; conducts life-history studies of birds and mammals; tests or devises methods of controlling populations of harmful birds or mammals; conducts bird and mammal disease investigations; conducts wildlife nutrition studies; formulates, conducts, or supervises a wildlife research program; studies plans for construction and operation of water-development projects to determine probable effects on wildlife resources; makes investigations in the fields of ornithology and mammalogy, involving the observation, collection, and classification of birds and mammals; superintends all activities in a given wildlife reserve.

33. *Wildlife Collector.* Procures various forms of animal life for museums, zoological gardens, laboratories, and hobbyists.

34. *Zoological Exhibit Curator.* Administers zoological exhibits, usually in a zoo, park, or other place where animals are kept for public exhibition; directs housing, feeding, and exhibition of animals; directs fiscal affairs of exhibits; gives technical advice on the care, exhibition, and collection of animals.

Chapter XV

Farming, Production, and Ranching

The time is at hand when a man would no more think of becoming a farmer without preparing for his vocation, than he would of becoming an engineer, a doctor, or a merchant without adequate training. In the old days, when land was plentiful, the population was scattered, the soil was fertile, and help was abundant and inexpensive, a man had a fair chance of being successful as a farmer without special training. Today, however, conditions have changed. Competition, location, transportation, marketing facilities, and many other controllable factors play an important role in the farmer's life. Although nature still does her part, the farmer now must study and plan to overcome the many obstacles that confront him daily. He must know about the life of plants and the functions of their parts, about soil and its relation to plant growth, about insects, bacteria, and fungi and their control. His mind must ever be open to new ideas. No longer is farming a matter of mere hard labor; it is a business to which one must bring scientific information, business principles, marketing know-how, and practical experience.

A scientific farmer ranks with the doctor, businessman, merchant, engineer, scientist, banker, carpenter, and mechanic. In fact, to some extent he must be all of these. He sells and buys, operates electrical equipment, treats his livestock, and applies science in selecting seed, fighting pests, or feeding livestock. He builds storage facilities and repairs machinery. Even with the growing specialization among farmers, it is probable that the average farmer is called upon, in the performance of his daily duties, to know a wider variety of things than any other businessman. A farmer cannot gain this knowledge merely by casual observation and the use of common sense. If modern farm machinery is to last, a farmer must be a mechanic. The tillage tools on the farm in former years consisted of a plow, a harrow, a cultivator, and a team of horses or mules. Today, a $20,000 combine, a $12,000 tractor, and other power equipment are complicated precision machines requiring mechanical skill and knowledge. Formerly, markets took care of themselves. Today, unless wisdom is practiced in choice of crops, limitation of production, and cooperative marketing, it may turn out that the more the farmer raises, the less net profit he makes. In short, modern farming demands a wide range of information if the farmer expects to remain in the channels of competition.

The modern farm is an efficient, tightly organized business operation which requires considerable capital. The average commercial farm today is valued at about $90,000, and this sum does not include equipment or livestock.

Qualifications of the Farmer

The man who runs such a farm must first, of course, be a good farmer, familiar with advanced farming practices. Beyond this, he must understand cost-price relationships, accounting, unit efficiency, machinery maintenance, conservation, animal or dairy husbandry (if he raises livestock), market demands and marketing methods, and consumer preferences—not to mention the application of chemicals to growing crops and the general utilization of new technological processes.

Ideally, then, the farmer must possess the abilities that a corporation president acquires by choosing well-trained assistants. Only very large farming operations can afford full-time assistants; and such assistants, like the boss himself, must combine several abilities and serve varied functions.

Some of today's successful older farmers have come up through the ranks, so to speak, without much formal education—but they have succeeded only because they have compensated for their lack of education by extra efforts to keep up with changing practices and methods. Tomorrow's farmer, it is certain, will have all the odds against him if he has neglected to acquire a basic education and special training for his chosen type of farming.

Capital Needed

Even to start as an independent farmer, the beginner will need a minimum of $30,000 to $50,000 capital to buy a farm. The alternative is to start on a commercial farm as an assistant, save his money, and eventually move into management and ownership. Many subscribe to the belief that the only way to get a good start in agriculture today is either to "inherit a farm or marry it."

Even the good all-round farmer cannot master all the special techniques of modern farming, but for the skills he lacks he can hire trained persons for almost any job. The multiplication of these specialized jobs partly accounts for the increasing opportunities in agriculture.

Specialists are available to inseminate cows, to dust a crop, to spray an orchard. Small farmers sometimes hire out to cut their neighbors' crops to help pay for the machinery their own farm production could not finance.

The following table gives statistics on several classes of farms, based on the value of farm products sold.

The nation's farmers are playing an increasingly important role in the general economy despite steadily declining prices for farm products.

The revolutionary changes that have been taking place in agriculture have made such a situation possible. The replacement of hand

INCOME OF FARM OPERATORS, 1960 CENSUS OF AGRICULTURE

Economic Class	Value of Farm Products Sold	No. of Farms, 1960 (1,000)	Average Value of Farm Products Sold Per Farm, 1960 (Dollars)	Average Cash Operating Expenses Per Farm, 1960 (Dollars)	Average Value Per Farm of Farm Products Sold Minus Cash Operating Expenses, 1960 (Dollars)
Commercial farms:					
Class I	$40,000 and over	106	95,235	72,824	22,411
Class II	$20,000 to $39,999	228	26,014	15,702	10,312
Class III	$10,000 to $19,999	490	13,599	7,586	6,013
Class IV	$5,000 to $9,999	591	7,090	3,804	3,286
Class V	$2,500 to $4,999	543	3,528	1,772	1,757
Class VI	$50 to $2,499[1]	307	1,379	599	781
Total, commercial farms		2,265	12,882	8,114	4,768
Other farms:					
Part-time	$50 to $2,499[2]	674	861	584	277
Part-retirement	$50 to $2,499[3]	311	927	487	440
Abnormal		3	34,640	30,983	3,656
Total, other farms		988	994	655	339
Total, all farms		3,253	9,268	5,847	3,422

[1] With operator under 65 years of age, working off farm less than 100 days and farm sales greater than other family income.
[2] With operator under 65 years of age, working off farm 100 days or more, or other family income exceeding farm sales.
[3] With operator 65 years of age or over.

ACREAGE AND VALUE OF MAJOR FARM CROP PRODUCTION[1]

1960

Crop	Acreage	Value (Dollars)
Corn	79,616,031	$4,384,427,694
Cotton	14,649,264	2,342,648,511
Hay	63,548,557	2,180,621,545
Wheat	49,566,924	1,871,910,772
Soybeans	23,070,254	1,034,901,533
Tobacco	1,108,274	947,626,032
Vegetables	3,490,763	739,626,458
Oats	26,572,824	638,797,378
Sorghum	17,927,257	577,465,717
Potatoes	1,200,431	414,995,928
Barley	14,199,311	343,301,247
Rice	1,617,037	249,380,338
Sugar Beets	911,796	187,339,907
Peanuts	1,468,231	140,963,017
Flaxseed	2,848,239	59,672,384
Sweet Potatoes	218,461	53,707,032
Rye	1,392,072	22,326,909
Cowpeas (Dry Peas)	179,423	5,973,756
Popcorn	131,169	5,302,884

INCOME AND VALUE OF MAJOR LIVESTOCK SALES[1]

1960

Dairy (Sold)	$7,832,434,195
Milk and Cream (Sold)	4,021,590,860
Cattle	7,163,482,171
Hogs	2,435,404,258
Poultry and Poultry Products	2,257,821,804
Sheep	337,995,732
Horses	52,189,375

[1] 1960 Census of Agriculture.

labor by machines and the merger of small farming units into larger ones to make the use of machinery economical have provided employment in factories to millions of people, many of whom have been forced off the farm.

This change has resulted in the expenditure of billions of dollars each year for farm machinery, equipment, buildings, and supplies. As a result, the activity of the nation's industrial plants is geared more closely to agriculture today than at any time in history.

Equipment Outlays

It is estimated that the farm investment in machinery is twice that of the entire steel industry and five times that of the automobile industry. To keep the 12,500,000 farm cars, trucks, and tractors running, the farmers buy some $1,500,000,000 of oil products each year, making them the petroleum industry's largest single customer.

In the days before mechanization, when animal power was used instead of tractors, expenditures by agriculture for industrial products was relatively small. Horses and mules were raised on the farms, as was the feed the animals consumed. In addition, the convenience equipment in the farmers' homes was rather primitive. But today, for the most part, the farms are equipped with refrigerators, electric ranges, washing machines, radio, television, and most of the home conveniences made by industry.

With this change in farming practices and living standards, the general economic position of the farmer has improved measurably. Recent figures indicate the farmers' total holdings are valued in excess of $203,000,000,000, and that $23,000,000,000 of this, or 11.5 per cent, is covered by debt. The average farm represents an investment in machinery alone of about $20,000 per worker, or nearly $4,000 per worker more than in industry.

Land prices continue at record levels, and this enables the small farmer to dispose of his holdings at an advantage. With the money received for his farm, he is able to buy a home in a nearby town and thus not present a relief problem, as did the earlier trek of tenant farmers to the cities.

Farm Income

With the farmer a key figure in the nation's economy, industry watches his gross income closely as an indication of what his purchasing power may be.

Cash receipts from farm marketings in a recent year were above $33,000,000,000. Compared with the figure of $9,100,000,000 in 1940, this represents an advance of more than three and one-half times.

Expenses of farm production have been rising steadily, reflecting increased costs for equipment, taxes, and almost every item going into the production of a crop. In 1962, farm production expenses were estimated at more than $28,000,000,000, compared with $6,700,000,000 in 1940.

Advantages and Disadvantages

Among the significant advantages of farming as a career are the following: Farming provides security; it allows one to be his own boss. The outdoor work is healthful, and there is a variety of work. Relatively small personal and family expenses are involved. The family can spend much time together, and children can be given responsibilities which teach them to work effectively. The farm is a good place to invest savings, and a desirable place to spend one's old age. Farmers live well compared with those in other occupations with comparable cash incomes; they live longer and are likely to enjoy their work more than city people do.

Among the disadvantages, these are commonly named: Considerable capital is needed to get a start. The income is uncertain and irregular, varying considerably from month to month. There is usually outdoor work to be done in bad weather. Those with training in agriculture must compete with untrained workers. It is difficult to arrange time for vacations. Formerly, isolation was cited as a disadvantage, but the improvement of roads, the development of electric and telephone systems, and the introduction of radios and televisions have done much to remove this objection.

How can you tell whether you should become a farmer? If you love the feel and fragrance of good, rich soil trickling through your fingers, you probably have an innate love of the land, and this is essential to a good farmer. The farmer must derive pleasure from growing things, both plant and animal, just as he must like people and want to help them. Finally, he must enjoy living and working outdoors.

If you do not have these interests, then try another career. But if you do have them, farming can provide a life that calls upon a man for intelligence, sweat, and compassion and rewards him with security, satisfaction, and spiritual peace.

A farmer has three great adversaries—climate, insects, and disease —but they are challenging enemies, and any life, to be full, must have problems. The conditions of the struggle require patience and courage; they also bind farmers together in a close neighborliness.

Training

How much education should a young person have to be a successful farmer? The more the better. As with everything else, a boy can be a successful farmer with a high-school education, but his chances are much better if he has attended college. He must know enough chemistry to handle soil and fertilizers; enough entomology to combat insect pests; enough plant and animal physiology and pathology to produce good stock and crops; and enough economics to market his produce profitably. All this he can learn at a good agricultural college. Generally, agricultural colleges cost less than other professional schools.

The majority of American farmers in the past have depended for their knowledge of farming on experience and on reading. Experts agree that no amount of formal training can replace practical experience as a basis for success; and it would be unwise for one who is not farm-reared to attempt farming as an occupation without first working as a hired hand on a well-operated farm.

Nevertheless, formal education to supplement farm experience is valuable. Vocational agriculture is taught in many high schools. Some states have schools of agriculture below the college level. Agricultural colleges provide training both for resident students and, through extension courses, for farmers. Resident students may take special short courses ranging in length from a few days to about two years; or they may take a four-year course leading to the bachelor's degree. A few prospective farmers take graduate work as well.

Getting Established in Farming

There are no legal or educational requirements regulating entrance to farming. Anyone who has the capital to rent or buy a farm may enter the occupation. Those with practical experience and formal training in agriculture have the greater chance for success.

Many young men still enter farming by way of the "agricultural stairway"—the sequence from farm boy to hired man to tenant to mortgaged owner to owner.

After weighing the pros and cons of farming versus other occupations and deciding in favor of the former, you are ready to consider the questions: What kind of farming shall I undertake? and Where shall I farm?

A wise choice takes many factors into account. To begin with, you should not buy or rent a farm unless you have had real experience in farming. You are almost certainly doomed to disappointment and failure if you undertake so complex a business without some experience on a good farm, under the guidance of a successful farmer. As a beginner you should gain experience as a hired man; then after a few years you may be in a position to manage your own farm.

Many experienced farmers stress the desirability of starting as a tenant rather than an owner. It is unwise to plunge into farming as an owner-operator until you have tried yourself out and know whether you like it as a business, whether you can make a success of it, and whether you have chosen the kind of farming and the location you want.

The region selected should be familiar, if possible. It is also helpful to settle where your family is known. The kind of agriculture that pays best in the vicinity should be a guide in determining the kind you enter. For example, Wisconsin is a leading dairy state, and a dairy farmer probably has a much better chance of success there than in an area where such farming is comparatively rare. Similarly, if you prefer poultry farming, a region known for successful commercial poultry farming should be chosen.

Do not select a type of farming that is unknown to the region; the soil or climate may be unfavorable and weight the odds against success.

In selecting a farm don't be guided solely by interested parties, such as a real-estate broker seeking a fee or a seller anxious to dispose of his property. Inquire fully into the past record of the farm, its yields, operating expenses, profits, and so on. Advice can usually be obtained without charge from such disinterested sources as county agricultural agents. State extension services, agricultural colleges, agricultural experiment stations, soil conservation services, and the various farm organizations can answer many of the pertinent questions.

The major hurdle for many young men with little money is where to get the cash to make a start in farming? It is true that farming is big business, but any farm boy who really wants to be a farmer can be one. The young man who really wants to get started in farming doesn't wake up suddenly when he is 21 and say, "Dad, how do I get the money to get started farming?" He began way back when he was 12 with a 4-H project, or at 15, when he was a member of the Future Farmers of America, with a calf. He received valuable experience working on a farm. He studied for it in vocational agriculture classes and gained experience in supervised projects. By the time he is 21 he probably owns some livestock and has money in the bank.

But more important than what he owns is what he has in his head and heart: His know-how, willingness to work and learn, and enthusiasm are what count with lenders, especially the financial institutions and those friends, relatives, and neighbors who finance many young farmers.

The average farmer—and it may be your dad—may increase his net income by 25 per cent if he uses all the tools of modern scientific farming. But the point is, if you want to farm, you must do a better-than-average-job, so make a deal with Dad and start on a career in farming. It takes two to make a successful father-son partnership, an understanding father and a son who is willing to work and knows what he wants. The best possible way for a young man to get started farming is to make a deal with his father or with a successful, understanding farmer in the community.

Job Descriptions in Farming, Production, and Ranching

1. *Dairy Farmer and Breeder.* Requires capital, experience, and initiative, and represents a worthy goal for many dairy-science graduates. Frequently, this goal is achieved only after gaining dairy-farm experience.

2. *Dairyman.* Handles all work pertaining to the care and management of a dairy herd. Is responsible for cleaning stables, cattle, and utensils; preparing feed and supplying it to the herd; milking, with its attendant duties of examining udders and checking milk for evidences of abnormal or disease conditions; keeping detailed records of feed consumption and cost, breeding and calving, milk production, sales, and purchases.

3. *Viniculturist.* Is responsible for supervising and carrying out vineyard operations, including the propagation, training, and pruning of the vines, the cultivation, irrigation, and fertilization of the vineyard, and the harvesting of the grapes. Instructs and supervises the vineyard laborers necessary at pruning and harvest time. Must be able to diagnose and control the diseases and pests attacking the vines,

to understand the economics of vineyard operations, and to take advantage of new growing and harvesting methods.

4. *Farmer.* Engages in the profitable exploitation of the soil to raise crops and animals, process them into salable form, and market them. The extent of his actual participation in the physical, supervisory, and administrative duties entailed depends largely on the size of the enterprise.

5. *Farm Manager.* Directs operations on large farm units, the proportion of his time given to managing as contrasted to performing farm operations depending upon the size of the unit.

6. *Farm Operator.* Is in charge of crop and livestock production, soil management, buying supplies, and selling products. Must be an able-bodied worker and also exercise good judgment as to the time schedule of the entire operation. The farm operator and his family live on the farm as well as work there.

7. *Fruit Grower.* Manages and operates a fruit orchard, his responsibilities including the spraying, pruning, and thinning of trees; irrigation of the orchard; the planting of new areas or replacement of old orchards; the supervision of picking, packing, storage, and marketing of fruit.

8. *Flock Manager—Poultry.* Utilizes training in poultry production business and finance to manage various types of poultry flocks such as broiler, hatchery supply, commercial egg, or replacement pullets, either individually or in multiple units. Is responsible for decisions on number of birds, time of replacement, and marketing.

9. *Florist, Wholesale Grower.* Produces general-line or specialty cut flowers, potted plants, and foliage plants for consignment to a florist commission house.

10. *General Manager, Farm.* Plans operations and supervises through foremen all activities connected with raising, harvesting, packing, and marketing farm products for corporations, cooperatives, and other owners of large operations. Studies market conditions to determine acreage allocations. Obtains credit from banks. Purchases seed, fertilizer, chemicals, tractors, and other farm equipment. Hires and discharges personnel. Prepares financial and other records. Periodically visits orchards and fields to inspect crops and estimate maturity dates. Determines when, where, and how to sell produce; contacts brokers and purchasers. May specialize in management of cooperative association, packing house, or public farm market.

11. *Livestock Farmer.* Must be familiar with the breeding, feeding, management, and disease control of livestock. Maintains and manages a herd of beef cattle, hogs, or sheep for the production of slaughter, feeder, or breeder livestock; performs all or some of the necessary duties depending on the size of the operation and the availability of labor, machinery, and equipment.

12. *Livestock Farm Manager.* Supervises or manages farming activities with livestock production, breeding, development, and marketing of purebred animals or the purchase and feeding of meat animals for the market.

13. *Nursery Owner.* Engages in the production and sale of all types of nursery stock—evergreens, shrubs, trees, flowers, bulbs, and fruit trees. Propagates and grows stock from small plants to finished product, including soil preparation, planting, culture, and maintenance. May be wholesaler or retailer. May specialize in landscaping.

14. *Poultryman.* Operates a farm for the production of eggs and/or meat from chickens, turkeys, ducks, and other domestic poultry. Work involves care and feeding of young and adult birds; sanitation; disease control through vaccination and medication; maintenance of equipment, such as feeders, waterers, and nests; collection, handling, and storing of eggs; maintenance of production records.

15. *Vegetable Gardener.* Grows vegetables for fresh market and for processing, including the growing of vegetables on intensively cultivated market gardens, on truck gardens located at a distance from market, and on general farms where vegetables are usually grown for sale or processing.

Chapter XVI

Food Technology and Processing

Food technology now provides challenging careers for many young men and women who are interested in the preserving and merchandising of farm products. The field deals with the scientific aspects of the handling, processing, manufacture, storage, distribution, and utilization of foods. As a food technologist, you would be applying many sciences, including biology, chemistry, microbiology, physics, physiology, psychology, and engineering, to your work in the food industry.

In modern living the purchase of prewashed, frozen, canned, dehydrated, and precooked foods is rapidly expanding. Today more than half of the consumer's food dollar goes to pay for processing, packaging, storage, and transportation. The marked technological progress that has taken place in our modern food industry has created a very large demand for men and women who have a thorough knowledge of the basic food sciences. This knowledge must be combined with ability in the technical processes of food production, manufacture, storage, and distribution. Today, food technologists are required in so many capacities that the demand for their services far exceeds the supply.

In addition to the various food industries concerned with the processing and distribution of cereals, dairy products, fruits and vegetables, meats, and other perishables, employment opportunities exist in state and Federal laboratories administering the food processing regulations, in colleges and universities, and in high-school and vocational teaching.

Quite naturally, the food industry is the greatest of all industries manufacturing products to sell. Whether in prosperity or depression people must eat, and since our population is growing at the rate of approximately 8,000 a day, the food industry must expand in the same ratio.

In the past twenty years the food industry has grown from a $16,000,000,000-a-year business to about $80,000,000,000 in 1963. By 1980, the projected increase in population will result in a $100,-000,000,000 to $125,000,000,000 food industry. The development of new products and the refinements of canning, preserving, freezing, and packaging have created new markets and added thousands of items to the shelves of our supermarkets.

Today's homemaker many select her groceries from an assortment of eight or nine thousand items, as compared with 1,000 items in the 1930s. Two-thirds of today's grocery-store items are either new or greatly improved in the past decade. Today's homemaker is asking for built-in maid services to lighten her work load and to provide the balanced, nutritious diet her family needs. The food industry is moving ahead because of the forward-looking management, new scientific knowledge, new foods, and new packaging techniques which food technologists have provided. These changes will continue in years to come, resulting in new jobs which require training in research, advertising, management, and marketing.

Despite the fact that food factories have decreased in numbers as they have become larger and more efficient, over 30,000 are currently in operation, producing more food, more efficiently, and with greater nutritional value. Over a billion dollars annually is spent to develop new processes, to improve existing foods, to install more efficient equipment and machinery, and to release the homemaker for a more leisurely life.

Doctors and nutritionists say that our nation's health is at an all-time high because our people eat wholesome, nutritious food. As a result, children are taller, sports records are broken annually, and the average life span of American men and women is constantly increasing. Our nation is composed of healthier people largely because of the work of the food technologist and nutritionist.

But elsewhere in the world, food—its production and processing—is a pressing problem. Every day we hear and see pictures of the tragic effects of lack of food and poor nutrition in the over-populated, under-developed countries across the oceans. The food technologist concerns himself with this problem from the field to the cannery, from the growing conditions through the preparation, processing, and preservation.

Opportunities

The vast amount of publicity given minerals, vitamins, and other food properties in recent years is stimulating added interest in areas concerned with producing, handling, processing, and distributing food and food products. Thousands of problems are waiting for chemists and other research workers with training in food technology. The future of foods is not all in research, however. The technologist may also assume responsibilities in the testing, manufacturing, demonstrating, packaging, and distributing of foods. In the future, many food technologists will be developing methods of dehydration for shipping of foods to foreign countries, solving such problems as the preservation of chlorophyll in dehydration, the retention of desirable flavors, and the elimination of undesirable odors.

The solving of one problem will stimulate interest in other areas. The food technologist may find himself writing, editing, selling, teaching, or conducting research for government agencies or commercial concerns.

Allied to the food industry is dairy technology, which includes the manufacture, storage, distribution, inspection, and researching of dairy products. Many fields are open to trained dairy technologists: manager, supervisor, or technician with a dairy firm; research technologist; college instructor; milk and dairy inspector for government or private industry; extension specialist; and many more. Trained dairy technologists with a little added study may expand their skills into biochemistry, fermentation chemistry, dairy bacteriology, mycology, protein chemistry, chemical engineering, food chemistry, sanitary engineering, heating and refrigeration engineering, and the special field of design, development, sales, and service of dairy equipment.

Animal technologists are trained to seek improvement in quality, preparation, grading, and economic production of such products as meat, animal hairs, wool, and hides. They may supervise grading and preparation of their products; a few teach, and many do analytical research. The extension specialist demonstrates methods of preparing and preserving foods. The livestock and wholesale meat-market reporter grades livestock and meats according to established meat standards.

Poultry scientists perform essentially the same duties as animal scientists but with such poultry products as eggs, dressed poultry, turkeys, ducks, and geese.

Horticulturists and home economists are finding a vast field for expansion in the development of frozen foods and modes of preservation. Food technology is an ideal training for men and women who demonstrate methods of preservation; sell the equipment necessary in preservation processes; do research such as perfecting and testing new recipes for food companies; or conduct radio, television, newspaper, or magazine programs and public relations efforts. The horticulturist in food technology follows his produce from the field through the cannery. The "field man" inspects and supervises the conditions under which his particular produce is grown. The horticulturist usually specializes in one particular fruit or vegetable. He may be employed by a processor to eliminate imperfections which Federal food inspectors may find in the produce.

Careers in Food Technology

The *food and nutritional chemist* studies the digestibility and biological values of foods, the composition of foods in respect to proteins, fats, carbohydrates, vitamins, and minerals. He also deals in the scientific formulation of diets to meet human and animal requirements. He may work in control or research, studying the processes taking place in the body for digestion and utilization of food.

The *food technologist* develops standard food products for food industries or chain stores that market their own brands. He may work in research in the line of frozen or dehydrated foods, or he may deal with consumers, seeking to determine their preferences as a guide for the manufacturer. He may specialize in horticulture, working on methods of preservation of fruit and vegetable products. Many food technologists are employed as sales, public relations, or management personnel; many others work for state or Federal inspection services.

The *nutritionist* teaches students the principles of nutrition and their application to the reproduction, growth, and health of all animals. He may conduct experiments in nutrition or assist students in their own research problems. He may be adviser to feed or food manufacturers, dealers or farmers on the formulation of diets for animals. If he has a talent for speaking and writing, his services may be in demand for lectures or scientific journals or newspapers.

The *food processor* works in a commercial operation, supplying retail stores with canned, frozen, dehydrated, or fermented fruits and vegetables. He may work in management, sales, quality control, or inspection and regulation.

The canning industry is one of the largest employers of food technologists today. Louis Pasteur's pioneering in the area of fermentation and Gail Borden's development of processes for condensation and hermetical sealing of milk opened doors to progress in food technology which still provide careers for thousands of graduates each year. Today the food industry demands far more skilled workers than America's agricultural colleges can provide.

The meat industry employs food technologists with training in chemistry, bacteriology, and meats. Thirty-two hundred meat-packing plants and processing industries today supply meat products for 30,000 retail stores and 500,000 eating places throughout the country. An army of meat inspectors, food technologists, and food processors insure the quality of meat products on the market today.

Food retailing and food distribution in general are areas which provide expanding opportunities for food technologists. The retailer helps American families to eat better for less money; he also helps the farmer to increase his income. Opportunities in food retailing include management or buying for large chain stores throughout the United States, as well as ownership and management of neighborhood groceries. Warehouse management and advertising also employ many graduates in food technology.

Job Descriptions in Food Technology and Processing

1. *Dairy Technologist.* Applies principles of bacteriology, chemistry, physics, engineering, and economics to development of new and improved methods of production, preservation, and utilization of milk and other dairy products. Conducts experiments in such areas as prevention of bacterial increase in milk during handling and processing, improvement of pasteurization methods, or the design of better packaging materials, dairy equipment, or supplies. May specialize according to product, as ice cream or cheese, or according to functional activity, as sanitation research or solving storage problems.

2. *Food Technologist.* Works in the fields of animal food products, crop food products, dairy food products, poultry food products, and food preservation and processing. Evaluates raw food products to determine standards of quality for processing purposes; develops methods for testing and measuring quality changes in food products re-

OPPORTUNITIES FOR PERSONS INTERESTED IN DAIRY TECHNOLOGY
Market Milk—Ice Cream—Butter—Cheese—Evaporated Milk—Powdered Milk

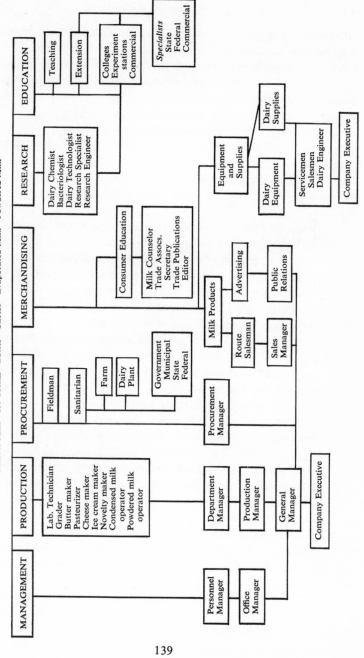

sulting from biological, chemical, or physical changes during processing, storage, handling, and transportation; develops techniques to control quality changes in food products and improve methods of preserving and processing food products. Makes use of principles of chemistry, bacteriology, and engineering in processing, manufacturing, and quality control of food products such as eggs, egg products, and fresh, frozen, and processed poultry meat products.

3. *Food Technician.* May be responsible for laboratory control or procedures for manufacturing concerns, including canning, dehydrating, freezing, brining, and other methods of preservation. Laboratory technicians are also employed by state and Federal inspection services.

4. *Food and Nutritional Chemist.* Studies the digestibility of foods; the biological values of foods; the composition of foods in respect to proteins, fats, carbohydrates, vitamins, and minerals; the distribution and storage of materials in the body; the chemical reactions occurring in the conversion of food materials into substances found in the body; the waste materials produced as a result of chemical reactions in the body; and the formulation of diets in chemical terms that will meet the requirements for the production of healthy, productive animals.

5. *Butter Maker.* Prepares cream for churning and churns it into butter; pasteurizes and ripens the cream; tests samples of butter for butter fat, salt content, and other properties. May be in complete charge of creamery, which requires a thorough knowledge of buttermaking, marketing, and seasonal conditions of raw products.

6. *Cheese Maker.* Checks milk and cultures used for hard or soft cheese, for quality. Cuts, cooks, and processes the cheese, putting it in suitable containers or packages. Requires both technical and practical knowledge.

7. *Cheese Milk Grader.* Grades milk by taste and smell and by running fast quality tests before it is dumped with other raw milk. Large plants usually have one man solely for this job. In smaller plants it may be done in conjunction with the dumping of the raw milk.

8. *Chemist, Assistant.* Performs various routine tests, such as filtration, titration, or precipitation, under supervision of a chemist; makes laboratory test reports and furnishes test data. Checks analy-

ses with specifications. Maintains supply of chemicals in a laboratory. Keeps laboratory equipment clean.

9. *Dairy Plant Manager.* Supervises one department which may process or manufacture: market milk, ice cream, butter, cheese, dry milk, evaporated milk, or special dairy products. As a rule works with and under supervision of general production manager.

10. *Dairy Plant Production Manager.* Supervises one or more departments making dairy products. Sees that each department has sufficient help and adequate raw materials and supplies, and that proper sanitation and the quality of all products is maintained. In a smaller plant, may be in charge of all processing; in a large plant may be in charge of only one or two departments.

11. *Dairy Bacteriologist.* Investigates activities of bacteria and other microorganisms in processing, spoilage, and transformation of milk and milk products. Isolates, cultures, and identifies microorganisms causing sourness of milk or improving flavor and keeping qualities of cheese, butter, and lactic beverages. Conducts research on action of microorganisms on whey and other milk constituents associated with production of alcohol and glycerine. Prepares tables or reports correlating fermentative reactions of isolated microorganisms in pure cultures with the flavor, body, age, and keeping qualities of cheeses and other dairy products.

12. *Dairy Biochemist.* Conducts research on the composition and nutritional changes during processing, packaging, and storing of dairy products; provides chemical control over raw materials, processes, and products; analyzes milk, butter, cheese, ice cream, and the materials used in processing dairy products; devises improved techniques and equipment used in manufacturing dairy products and studies the utilization of dairy by-products as food.

Chapter XVII

Government Careers for Agricultural Graduates

One out of every eight workers in the United States was employed as a civilian worker by the Federal, state, or local government in 1960. More than half of these workers were employed by local government units, about a fifth by state governments, and the remainder —over 2,000,000—worked for the Federal government. These figures do not include the 2,800,000 persons who were serving in the various branches of the Armed Forces.

Government service is one of the nation's largest fields of employment. Several hundred thousand persons are hired each year for Federal, state, and local government jobs all over the country.

Government Activities

About one-third (2,500,000) of all government workers are engaged in providing educational services. The great majority of these employees work for state and local government as teachers, counselors, librarians, dietitians, nurses, administrators, clerks, office workers, maintenance, and auxiliary workers. Elementary and secondary schools employ the largest numbers.

The second-largest group of government workers were engaged in national defense activities of the Federal government. This group included the civilian employees of the Department of Defense and a few other related agencies. The workers served as administrators, clerical employees, scientists, engineers, and manual workers in hospitals, naval yards, arsenals, and schools provided by the military services.

There are more than 500,000 workers in health services, hospitals, the postal system, highways, and general control functions such as legislative bodies, justice department, tax enforcement, financial activities, and general administration.

MAJOR FUNCTIONS OF GOVERNMENT WORKERS . . . .

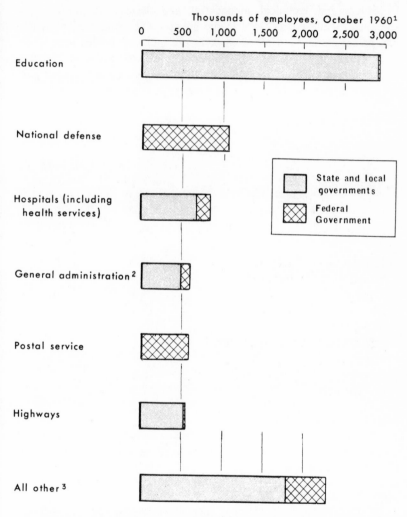

[1] All Federal civilian employees, including those outside United States and 34,000 employees of the National Guard paid directly from the Federal Treasury.

[2] Includes legislative, judicial, tax, and other financial and general administrative activities.

[3] Includes police protection, administrators of natural resources, and all other services not elsewhere classified.

Source: U.S. Bureau of the Census.

Employment by Categories

More than 4,000,000 government workers in 1960 were employed in professional, technical, managerial, and clerical occupations—the so-called "white-collar" jobs in the government agencies. The teachers, postal clerks, and office workers are included in this area.

Approximately 3,000,000 persons were classified as craft, service, and manual workers. The following chart shows a comparison of government workers to all employed workers in the United States.

Category	Percent of	
	Government workers in the U.S.	All employed workers in the U.S.
All categories	100.0	100.0
Professional and technical	33.7	11.2
Managers, and officials and proprietors	5.3	10.6
Clerical and kindred workers	23.4	14.7
Sales workers	.2	6.6
Craftsmen, foremen, and kindred workers	8.7	12.8
Operatives and kindred workers	5.6	18.0
Service workers	17.8	12.5
Laborers	5.2	5.5
Farmers and farm workers	.2	8.1

Note: Because of rounding, sums of the individual items may not equal 100 per cent.

Agricultural Workers in Federal Agencies

In addition to the vocational agriculture teachers and county extension agents, who are usually employed by public schools and state agencies, there are a number of attractive career opportunities in the United States Department of Agriculture. The department was established in 1862 and presently employs approximately 72,000 persons on a full-time basis as well as a limited number of student trainees for summer work. The department employs agronomists; bacteriologists; b' logists; botanists; chemists; conservationists; economists, including agricultural economists; agricultural engineers; entomologists; farm managers; foresters; horticulturists; animal scientists; inspectors; marketing specialists; plant pathologists; soil scientists, and technologists.

The several agencies and subagencies in the Department of Agriculture are:

1. Agricultural Economics, Washington 25, D.C. Employs 2,800 persons, principally agricultural economists and agricultural statisticians.

2. Agricultural Research Service, Hyattsville, Maryland 20781. Carries out research on crops, farm and land management, livestock, human nutrition, and home economics. Develops new and expanded uses for farm commodities; conducts control and regulatory programs, including plant and animal quarantine, meat inspection, and others. Employs 16,000 persons, with some summer employment.

3. Northern Regional Research Laboratory, 1815 North University, Peoria, Illinois. Employs 400 scientists with masters and doctors degrees.

4. Eastern Utilization Research and Development Division, 600 East Mermaid Lane, Philadelphia, Pennsylvania. Employs 350 biochemists, chemists, engineers, and physicists with masters and doctors degrees.

5. Southern Utilization Research and Development Division, 1100 Robert E. Lee Building, P.O. Box 7307, New Orleans, Louisiana. Employs 400 to 500 chemists, cotton technologists, engineers, and physicists.

6. Western Utilization Research and Development Division, 800 Buchanan St., Albany, California. Employs 350 persons for research and development on agricultural commodities and some summer employment.

7. Agricultural Stabilization and Conservation Service, Washington, D.C. 20250. Is responsible for acreage allotments and marketing quotas, to help keep supplies in line with demand; feed-grain program, to divert corn, barley, and grain sorghum acreage to conservation use; wheat stabilization program, to divert part of wheat acreage allotment to conservation use; conservation reserve, to divert general cropland from annual crops to conservation use; price support for

numerous commodities; reduction of surpluses through sales, barter, transfer, donation, and other means; helping obtain adequate farm and commercial storage for farm products; administering the Sugar Act, the National Wool Act, and the International Wheat Agreement; administering marketing agreement and order programs for milk, tobacco, and other commodities; investigating and meeting conditions that threaten or result in national disasters and emergencies requiring assistance. Employs 300 persons for data processing.

8. Farmers Home Administration, South Agricultural Building, Washington, D.C. 20225. Employs 5,000 persons for offices throughout the United States to provide farmers with credit and guidance in sound farm and home management.

9. Foreign Agricultural Service, 14th Street and Independence Avenue, S.W., Washington, D.C. 20250. Administers U.S.D.A. foreign programs in the interests of U.S. agriculture, with special emphasis on market promotion abroad. Attachés at 55 foreign posts maintain a constant flow of world agricultural intelligence. Employs 900 persons for positions in Washington, D.C., and overseas positions. Seeks agricultural economists.

10. Forest Service, South Agricultural Building, Washington, D.C. 20250. Conducts research on growing and harvesting timber; improving water and range resources; protecting forests from fire, insects, and disease; the use of wood products and development of new ones; and improvement in methods of marketing forest products. Employs 20,000 persons with a few additional for summer. Seeks architects (landscape), biologists (wildlife), business administrators, economists, engineers, entomologists, foresters, geneticists, pathologists (forest), range conservationists, soil scientists, and technologists (forest).

11. Forest Products Laboratory, South Agricultural Building, Washington, D.C. 20250. Employs 400 persons to conduct research on utilization of wood and wood products.

12. Office of Information, 14th St. and Independence Ave., S.W., Washington, D.C. 20250. Seeks writers, editors, and specialists to disseminate information on U.S.D.A. programs and services to the public. Some summer employment.

13. Rural Electrification Administration, 14th St. and Independence Ave., S.W., Washington, D.C. 20250. Employs 1,000 persons

to work in financing of telephone and electric service to farmers and others in rural areas.

14. Soil Conservation Service, 14th St. and Independence Ave., South Building, Washington, D.C. 20250. Employs 15,000 persons to provide technical assistance to landowners and farmers in carrying out the national soil and water conservation program. Classifies soils in a nationwide system; studies soils in the laboratory to determine their properties and how they respond to different treatments. A number of agriculture and engineering students are employed for summer work. Positions available include agricultural economists, agronomists, engineers (agricultural and civil), geologists, range conservationists, soil scientists, and wildlife biologists.

Other Federal departments which employ a limited number of agricultural college graduates are the following:

15. Department of Commerce, 14th St. and Constitution Avenue, Washington, D.C. 20230.

16. Bureau of the Census, Washington, D.C. 20233.

17. Department of the Air Force, Washington, D.C. 20225. Employs 350,000 civilians.

18. Department of the Army, Washington, D.C. Employs 370,000 civilians for worldwide employment.

19. Marine Corps, Washington, D.C. 20280. Employs 17,000 civilians for headquarters and regional offices.

20. Department of the Navy, Washington, D.C. 20260. Employs 360,000 persons for work at headquarters and throughout the world.

21. Food and Drug Administration, Washington, D.C. 20204. Employs 3,000 persons to administer Federal food, drug, and cosmetic laws. Agricultural college graduates with courses in chemistry, bacteriology, and other biological sciences are employed as food and drug inspectors.

22. Public Health Service, 330 C St., S.W., Washington, D.C. 20225. Employs 30,000 persons. Seeks biologists, biochemists, writers, management trainees, and social scientists with agricultural training.

23. Bureau of Commercial Fisheries, 18th and C Sts., N.W., Washington, D.C. 20240. Seeks economists and fishery biologists.

24. Bureau of Indian Affairs, 18th and C Sts., N.W., Washington, D.C. 20240. Employs 12,000 persons to provide various services to Indians. Agricultural graduates are considered for careers as apprais-

ers, agricultural engineers, foresters, range conservationists, social workers, soil scientists, and teachers.

25. National Park Service, 18th and C Sts., N.W., Washington, D.C. 20240. Employs 6,000 persons for work in National Parks as naturalists, landscape architects, park historians, and rangers.

26. Bureau of Sport Fisheries and Wildlife, 18th and C Sts., N.W., Washington, D.C. Seeks biologists, fish hatchery managers, and refuge managers.

27. Peace Corps, 806 Connecticut Ave., N.W., Washington 25, D.C. Seeks agricultural scientists, bacteriologists, biologists, agricultural engineers, 4-H workers, foresters, natural scientists, social scientists, and veterinarians.

Student Trainee Program

The student trainee program offers the college student employment before graduation. Student trainees are employed at the GS-3 level if they have completed one year of college and at the GS-4 level if they have completed two and a half years of college.

Approximately 200 student trainees are employed by the Soil Conservation Service during the summer. Students with the following majors are eligible: agricultural engineering, civil engineering, geology, range conservation, soil conservation, and soil science.

Each summer, the Foreign Agricultural Service employs approximately five student trainees majoring in agricultural economics. Interested students should file for the examination and write Personnel Office, Foreign Agricultural Service, U.S. Department of Agriculture, Washington, D.C. 20225.

Other agencies in the department employ approximately 40 student trainees during the summer. Jobs may be available in the following specialties: agricultural economics, agricultural statistics, engineering (agricultural and civil), farm management supervision, geology, home economics, plant pest control, range conservation, and soil science (research).

To file for student trainee, submit application card form 5000 AB to the appropriate Regional Civil Service Commission Office.

Job Opportunities in U.S.D.A.

1. *Administrative Trainee.* Works in budget, personnel, supply management, automatic data processing, management analysis, business management, and related administrative services.

2. *Agricultural Commodity Grader.* Inspects and grades commodities to United States standards and various other quality and condition specifications. Evaluates defects resulting from disease, transit, storage, or handling and prepares and issues official grade certificates for shippers, receivers, venders, or others having a financial interest in the commodities involved.

3. *Agricultural Economist.* In the Economic Research Service, conducts studies in foreign and domestic marketing, production, farm finances and taxation, land utilization, international agriculture, and land and water conservation.

4. *Agricultural Economist.* In the Soil Conservation Service, collects and analyzes economic data; estimates flood damages and costs and benefits that may accrue from improvements; and determines the ratio of benefits to costs of proposed improvements.

5. *Agricultural Economist.* In the Foreign Agricultural Service, collects, interprets, and analyzes agricultural statistics and economic data relating to American and foreign agricultural production and marketing. After a period of training and experience in Washington, D.C., may be assigned to overseas service as agricultural attaché or assistant agricultural attaché.

6. *Agricultural Engineer (Research).* Studies crop harvesting and processing, tillage and soil mechanics, crop growing, livestock production, farm structures, and the application of electrical energy to agriculture.

7. *Agricultural Market Reporter.* Assembles data and information relating to the purchase and sale of bulk or processed agricultural commodities; prepares reports and analyses designed to show status and progress of various marketing programs; compiles data for pricing commodities; settles claims; and plans the movement of agricultural commodities.

8. *Agricultural Marketing Specialist.* Develops and administers price stabilization programs concerned with acreage, yield, and production trends in the various producing areas; probable utilization of the commodity; possible new uses that might be developed; chances for improving storability of stocks; effect of disposal of large quantities on domestic and foreign price structures; types of storage best suited to the particular commodities involved; programs carried on by other government agencies; and changes in the controlling legislation.

9. *Analytical Statistician (Agriculture)*. Analyzes economic and statistical data including agricultural prices and income, short-range and long-range projections, outlook for farm commodities, food demand and consumption; and develops new statistical techniques for the measurement of economic relationships.

10. *Animal Husbandman, Animal Physiologist, Parasitologist, and Dairy Husbandman*. Employed by the Agricultural Research Service to conduct research on the following projects: livestock production; improvement of methods of breeding, nutrition, and management of beef and dairy cattle, swine, poultry, sheep, and goats; and testing of control measures for parasites of livestock and poultry. Approximately nine of these positions are filled each year.

11. *Entomologist*. Performs research on insects affecting crops, man, and animals; abundance, distribution, and identification of insects; transmission of plant diseases; plant resistance to insect attack; cultural, mechanical, biological, and chemical controls; beneficial insects.

12. *Farm Management Supervisor*. In the Farmers Home Administration, makes and supervises loans to farmers for many purposes: farm operation, farm ownership, water development and soil conservation, rural housing, watersheds, and emergencies resulting from drought, floods, and other such conditions. The farm management aspect of this work involves providing borrowers with advice and guidance on farm and home management to enable them to make profitable use of their land, labor, capital, and other resources.

13. *Field Representative*. In the Rural Electrification Administration, assists loan applicants, assures the security of Federal loans, and provides borrowers with information and services needed to help them meet loan obligations and to develop successful independent business enterprises.

14. *Research Forester*. Assigned to four main kinds of projects: forest management, forest economics, watershed management, and forest protection. The primary objective is to lay the scientific foundation for management of forest lands that will provide adequate supplies and suitable quality of timber for national needs by protecting timber crops from fire, insects, and disease, as well as the regulation of streamflow and the prevention of erosion. Research is also conducted to improve outdoor recreation and scenic benefits.

15. *Forest Products Technologist.* Employed under the Forest Service research program to study how wood and wood products can be better utilized and how waste can be reduced. Programs are carried out at ten regional forest and range experiment stations, at the Forest Products Laboratory at Madison, Wisconsin, and at more than a hundred smaller research centers.

16. *Inspector.* Employed by the Inspector General from persons with backgrounds in law or accounting who qualify through the Federal Service Entrance Examination, the Management Intern option of that examination, or other appropriate examinations.

17. *Investigator.* Employed by the Office of the Inspector General to audit agency activities and programs and investigate irregularities; position requires traveling about 90 per cent of the time.

18. *Operations Assistant.* Employed by the Agricultural Stabilization and Conservation Service. Explains new programs or major changes within existing ones; performs special assignments throughout the state and carries out detailed review and examination of program operations in the county offices.

19. *Operations Trainee.* Appointed by the Rural Electrification Administration from persons who have qualified on the Federal Service Entrance Examination and have majored in business administration, accounting, public administration, economics, or other appropriate subjects. Performs duties in rural electrification and telephone programs involving operation, management, accounting, loan appraisal, and related work.

20. *Plant Physiologist.* Performs research in effects on plants of light, temperature, moisture, nutrients, and natural and applied chemicals; physical and chemical properties; and composition of plants as related to soil and atmospheric environment.

21. *Plant Pest Control Inspector.* In the Agricultural Research Service, participates in a nationwide plant pest control program involving surveys, cooperative control operations, regulatory operations, and methods of improvement.

22. *Plant Quarantine Inspector.* Enforces Federal plant quarantine. Receives an intensive six-month training course before assignment.

23. *Program Specialist.* Recommends adaptations of programs such as price supports, production adjustments, agricultural conser-

vation, and grain storage; conducts and attends training meetings on the provisions, objectives, and operations of all phases of agricultural conservation and stabilization programs.

24. *Range Conservationist.* Employed by the Soil Conservation Service and the Forest Service. Assists landowners and operators in determining the suitability of their land for the production of forage and other crops; develops plans to insure the use of conservation practices needed to improve ranges and pastures.

25. *Soil Conservationist.* Employed by the Soil Conservation Service to prepare conservation plans for landowners and operators involving the use and treatment of land according to its needs and capabilities and the types of operations to be performed on it. Provides on-site technical assistance. Approximately 115 soil conservationists are employed annually.

26. *Soil Scientist.* Performs research in chemical, physical, and microbiological properties of plants and soils; soil management practices to improve crops, including fertilizing, green manuring, liming, tilling, managing residues, irrigating, and draining; methods of evaluating physical and chemical conditions of soil affecting crop production.

FEDERAL CIVIL SERVICE COMMISSION OFFICES

Addresses	*Jurisdiction*
Central Office—United States Civil Service Commission, Washington, D.C. 20225.	Washington, D.C.; Alexandria, Virginia; Arlington and Fairfax counties, Virginia; Prince George and Montgomery counties, Maryland; and overseas areas, except the Pacific.
Atlanta Region—Atlanta Merchandise Mart, 240 Peachtree Street, N.W., Atlanta 3, Georgia.	North Carolina, South Carolina, Georgia, Florida, Alabama, Tennessee, and Mississippi.
Boston Region—Post Office and Courthouse Building, Boston 9, Massachusetts.	Maine, New Hampshire, Vermont, Massachusetts, Rhode Island, and Connecticut.
Chicago Region—Main Post Office Building, Chicago 7, Illinois.	Wisconsin, Michigan, Illinois, Ohio, Indiana, and Kentucky.
Dallas Region—114 Commerce Street, Dallas 2, Texas.	Texas, Louisiana, Oklahoma, and Arkansas.

FEDERAL CIVIL SERVICE COMMISSION OFFICES—CONTINUED

Addresses	Jurisdiction
Denver Region—Building 41, Denver Federal Center, Denver, Colorado.	Arizona, New Mexico, Utah, Wyoming, and Colorado.
New York Region—220 East 42nd Street, New York 17, New York.	New York and New Jersey.
Philadelphia Region—Customhouse, Second and Chestnut Streets, Philadelphia 6, Pennsylvania.	Pennsylvania, Delaware, West Virginia, Virginia (except Arlington and Fairfax counties and Alexandria), and Maryland (except Prince George and Montgomery counties).
St. Louis Region—1256 Federal Building, St. Louis 3, Missouri.	Missouri, Kansas, Minnesota, North Dakota, South Dakota, Nebraska, and Iowa.
San Francisco Region—128 Appraisers Building, 630 Sansome Street, San Francisco 11, California.	California, Nevada, Hawaii, and the Pacific overseas area.
Seattle Region—302 Federal Office Building, Seattle 4, Washington.	Montana, Oregon, Idaho, Washington, and Alaska.

Chapter XVIII

Plant Science—Agronomy, Botany, Forestry, Horticulture

Plant science is that area of the biological and earth sciences that deals with agronomy, botany, forestry, and horticulture as they concern separate groups of plants.

The plant scientist plays an important role in the life of our country. The development of many new products has been stimulated by the search for new markets for farm produce. The scientific facts of plant life are so broad that more people are being urged to enter the field. The opportunities for specialization are numerous.

A young man or woman with an excellent academic record who has the capacity to weigh evidence and arrive at sound conclusions from experimental data will have no difficulty in finding employment. Attractive salaries are being paid by corporations for the services of men with unusual ability, training, and reputation.

The person interested in plant science may develop his interests along a specialization in agricultural biochemistry, agronomy, botany, or horticulture. The field is broad and appeals alike to men and women. There is a place for many additional kinds of research in agriculture.

The trend in recent years has been toward a finer subdivision of the sciences into new specialties, many of which offer great opportunities in teaching, research, and testing of plant varieties, cultural practices, and production of new varieties.

There is also a trend toward higher training requirements in all the plant sciences. The demand for research workers has resulted in greater specialization and more advanced degrees for persons interested in research and development of new plant varieties to meet future needs.

Plant scientists study the structure of plants and trees, their life processes, and the relation between plants and their environment. The number and variety of plants is so immense and the life processes are so varied and complex that plant scientists must of necessity become specialists.

AGRONOMY AND SOIL SCIENCE

Agronomy is the application of scientific principles to soil management and crop production. The field of soil management is concerned with the character and origin of soils, their properties, fertility, cultivation, and conservation; the study of crop production includes their growth, breeding, and improvement.

Agronomy, in its broadest meaning, is concerned with the technical aspects of plant, soil, and related sciences and their application to field crop production, soil management and improvement, crop improvement, and utilization. In many of the Land-Grant Colleges, departments of agronomy include soil science as well as crop science.

The original distinction between agronomy and horticulture was that the former dealt with crops grown in the field and the latter with garden and orchard crops. This distinction no longer prevails, since many so-called garden crops such as lettuce, onions, and peas are grown today as field crops but are dealt with by the horticulturist. Some agronomists, however, carry out research in a few of these field crops.

Soil science is the scientific study of the nature, distribution, origin, conservation, and improvement of soils, and the application of scientific principles to their management for plant production and other purposes.

Agronomy involves the scientific study of field crops as related to their production, breeding, improvement, and utilization. Objectives in such studies are to develop methods for the most efficient production, management, and utilization of field crops as well as to improve existing varieties with reference to soil and climatic adaptation, disease and insect pests, and other characteristics leading toward sustained or increased production of high-quality products.

Agronomists and soil scientists may specialize along regional lines as well as by crops or by other fields of specialization. Such regional specialization calls for familiarity with the major crops or soil types of the region.

An agronomist or a soil scientist may specialize in one or more of the following functions:

1. Research through scientific experiments and field surveys into the nature, origin, management, distribution, use, conservation, and improvement of soils; and into crop production, improvement, and utilization. Other studies include flood control and construction as these relate to soils.
2. Consulting work regarding soil characteristics in relation to its uses in construction and in planning foundations and subgrades, and for commercial agricultural companies.
3. Extension of principles of crop and soil science through demonstration and education, including the planning of demonstration farms and direct assistance to farmers and other land users.
4. Teaching in colleges, universities, and technical schools.
5. Management of production, sales, service, and distribution of fertilizers, soil amendments, soil inoculants, seeds; also of large-scale plantations, particularly in the tropics.
6. Others (a) appraisal of soil productivity and rural land evaluation; (b) technical writing, usually in connection with other functions; and (c) crop estimates and appraisal of crop damage.

Crop Science

The agronomist, crop scientist, or other specialist working in this field carries out scientific experiments to develop methods for the most efficient production and utilization of field crops. He studies methods of seed-bed preparation, suitable plant varieties, botanical relationships, methods of cultivation, soil and fertilizer requirements, time and method of planting, effects of rotation of crops, harvesting and marketing of crops, and control of crop enemies (diseases, insects, animals). To develop such methods he performs experimental work on the resources of plants to their environment, such as the effect of temperature, nutrition, rainfall, humidity, length of day, sunlight, and storage conditions on quality, quantity, time of ripening, and other characteristics of agronomic crops. He also studies the effect of soil, drainage, altitude, weeds, and wind on crop plants. He takes into account factors such as conservation of soil and of its fertility in any crop production program with which he may deal. In these studies he draws upon his knowledge of the fundamental principles of plant physiology, plant pathology, entomology, soil science, and other fields, because they are all involved and interrelated in the growth and production of the crop. It is often to his advantage to be familiar with modern field plot design and statistical analysis of experimental results. The various fields of study listed above can be applied to any of the crops and crop groups listed below.

Fields of Specialization

Cereal Crops. Deals with small grains, wheat, oats, barley, rye, and rice, corn, grain sorghum, and the oil crop flax.

Leguminous Crops. Deals with alfalfa, clovers, lespedeza, and kudzu for hay, silage, and pasture; soybeans and peanuts for forage, seed, and oil; and cover crops such as Austrian winter peas, field beans, vetches, and lupines. Seed production of many of the small-seeded legumes presents special problems, and their use in conservation practices is an important phase of crop production.

Forage Crops (other than legume). Deals with the hay and pasture crops, which for the most part belong to the grass family, such as brome grass, crested wheat grass, orchard grass, and timothy and Kentucky bluegrass in the north; Bermuda grass, dallis grass, bahia grass, Johnson grass and others in the southern states. Such cereal crops as oats, barley, and sorghum and corn, when grown for hay or silage, fall into this group. In addition there are a number of native grasses of great importance in range and livestock production. The best use of these crops in rotation and for soil conservation and animal production constitutes an important study.

Cotton. Deals with most of the activities discussed in the summary and also with other crops grown in rotation with cotton, such as peanuts.

Sugarcane. Deals with the problems of crop production under tropical or semitropical conditions, with methods of vegetative propagation, and with special problems in planting, culture, and harvesting.

Sugar Beets and Other Root Crops. Deals with sugar beets or other root crops such as turnips and mangoes. When grown as field crops, these are the concern of the agronomist; as garden crops, they are usually dealt with by the horticulturist.

Turf and Other Special Grass Culture. Deals with development of breeding and management methods relating to the seeding and maintenance of fine turf, heavy-duty vegetation, and grasses that control sand-blowing or tie down the soil on embankments. Develops soil management techniques which can be used to build a soil on which vegetation will grow on excavations, fills, subsoils, and under other adverse conditions. In developing new methods or in making recommendations, he carries out experiments or uses his knowledge of the use of lime, fertilizers and soil amendments, surface mulch and composting, and of soil treatment to effect good drainage, improve the retention of moisture in droughty soils and improve quality and structure. In this work the agronomist uses his knowledge of plants and the adaptability of particular species for different conditions and uses. He develops methods of establishment of a turf, including the time, manner, and rates of planting, soil treatments for disease and insect control, and methods of management to maintain vegetation in good condition at all times.

Noxious Weed Control. Deals with the development of methods and practices for the control of noxious weeds on farms, banks of irrigation ditches, and public lands, using his knowledge of the growth and seeding habits of weeds and of crops, the effect of chemicals on soils and plants, and the use of smother crops, sod crops, crop rotation, and tillage methods on weed control. He carries out experiments to determine the value of new or inadequately tested weed-killing elements or compounds, and assists farmers in planning for the best use of their land.

Other Specialties. Such crops as potatoes, sweet potatoes, rubber plants, drug plants, hemp, and fiber flax may be classed as either horticultural or agronomic crops, depending upon the manner and the region in which they are grown.

Soil Science

The soil scientist is primarily a research worker in field and laboratory; a teacher in colleges, universities, or technical schools; an adviser in soil use and manipulation for construction; or an adviser in rural land use and management.

He is concerned with the fundamental principles of soil origin, distribution, composition, chemical properties, and behavior and their application to individual soil management practice, crop production, farming systems, and to community enterprises that influence the soil or limit the alternative uses of soil.

Fields of Specialization

Soil Fertility and Management. Deals with the application of the principles of agronomy and soil chemistry to the production of crops and the maintenance of soil productivity through the use of fertilizer, lime, composts, manure and other soil amendments, and cover and green manure crops. He relates the use of these materials to local soil characteristics; to tillage, crop rotation, and other farm practices; and to the requirements of particular crops.

Soil Conservation. Deals with the application of principles of soil science and agronomy to the planning of crop rotation; soil management practices such as strip cropping and contour plowing; land use on the farm unit; and reforestation, as these relate to the conservation of soil and water.

Soil Genesis, Classification and Mapping. By means of field trips, laboratory examination, and controlled experimentation, studies soil morphology, genesis (processes of soil formation), classification, and productivity; and develops and carries out programs of classifying and mapping soils. He evaluates the response of various soil types to management practices, and the adaptability of various crops to different soils.

Soil Chemistry and Mineralogy. Deals with the application of principles of chemistry, mineralogy, and agronomy to the problems of soil classification, formation, and composition; and to soil problems encountered in crop production and soil management.

Soil Microbiology. Deals with the application of the principles and methods of microbiology and chemistry to studies of microbiological processes; problems affecting crop production, such as decomposition of organic matter by action of bacteria and fungi, and nitrogen fixation; soil fertility and management; soil and water conservation; soil genesis, morphology, and classification; and the production and use of soil inoculants.

Soil Physics and Mechanics. Deals with the application of the methods and principles of physics to soil problems encountered in crop production, soil classification, drainage, irrigation practices, and soil and water conservation and use; and problems of soil stabilization and drainage in construction of roads, dams, buildings, and other structures.

BOTANY

Many people thing that botany consists exclusively of collecting and identifying plants. This was true in earlier centuries, but in botany, as in all scientific fields, continuing research has brought tremendous growth to our knowledge of plants and their structure and activities. Along with increasing knowledge has come a vast array of new challenges and problems. Nowadays, the identification of plants is just as necessary as formerly, especially in countries in which the flora is not yet well known, but botanists are no longer just collectors.

The botanist teaches basic plant sciences such as plant physiology, genetics, or classification, in colleges and universities; or he is a research worker in such fundamental studies as plant development, heredity, ecology, structure, or classification. He often combines field and laboratory work. He uses microscopes and staining processes in studying cells and tissues, or complex apparatus to learn more about plant functions. He often maintains a collection of dried or preserved plants to aid in identification of specimens.

For a thorough appreciation of the work of plant scientists, one must consider what this world would be like had there been no botanists. There would be fewer people, because many would have died of disease, and those who survived would be both less healthy and more hungry. In addition, many plant varieties would not exist, and our understanding of life would be less complete.

The discoveries of botanists have contributed to an understanding of man and animals, and in some cases have contributed to the physical sciences as well. Plants provide more suitable experimental material for the study of fundamental biological questions than do animals.

Botanists study plant cells, structure, function, inheritance, diseases, chemical components, relationships of plants to the environment and other organisms, and other more specialized areas. Some botanists are concerned with practical problems, as in forestry, horticulture, agronomy, conservation, allergy, and floriculture. In addition to academic positions, botanists find employment in industry and in government.

To prepare for challenging careers in botany, high-school students should take all possible biology courses, plus a good background in English, mathematics, physical sciences, and one or more foreign languages. College students should get further training in those fields noted above and, in addition to taking specialized courses in botany, should broaden their background with appropriate courses in zoology, geology, biochemistry, and bacteriology. The advice of a competent botanist is indispensable in planning the college program. In addition, most experts agree that a broad general education, including the social sciences and humanities, is of value to the professional botanist, giving him breadth in his vocation and preparing him for his role as a citizen.

The four-year course leading to the bachelor's degree will prepare one for teaching in high school (if state certification requirements have been met) and for many types of position in industry and government, as well as for positions as technical assistant in academic institutions. However, graduate work leading to a master's or Ph.D. degree is required for most research and academic positions. A "B" average in undergraduate work is frequently required for admission to graduate school, and competence in one or more foreign languages is usually required for graduate degrees.

Plant Pathology

Plant pathologists deal with the nature, cause, and control of diseases of plants and seek to protect field crops, vegetables, fruits, ornamental plants, and plant products from damage or destruction by infectious fungi (molds, mildews, smuts), bacteria, viruses, or physiological disorders. They study both healthy and diseased plants and try to determine the nature of the disease-causing agent and the influence of temperature, humidity, sunshine, and soil on the agent. Pathologists go into affected areas to find out what plants or insects harbor or spread the disease and what varieties of a crop are most resistant to the disease. They test various methods of prevention and control of a disease under both laboratory and field conditions.

All plants, both cultivated and wild, are subject to attack by innumerable diseases caused by fungi, bacteria, nematodes, and viruses very similar to those causing disease in man and the lower animals. All sorts of plants and perishable plant products are likewise subject to physiological disorders, injury, or deterioration from such causes as extremes of heat, cold, moisture, drought, or wind; excessive or insufficient supplies of various mineral nutrients or other chemicals in the soil; noxious gases; or unfavorable storage conditions.

Qualifications of Plant Pathologists. Professional plant pathologists are basically trained in the plant sciences. They are especially trained in mycology (study of fungi) and bacteriology and usually have additional preparation in plant physiology, plant structure, microscopic plant anatomy, genetics, statistical methods, and modern languages.

They often have some training in one or more of the following: horticulture, agronomy, soils, silviculture, entomology, and biochemistry. The generally accepted minimum requirement for an assistantship or professional trainee position in plant pathology is a bachelor's degree, with a major in plant pathology; but full professional status, in which investigational work is carried out independently, generally requires a doctor's degree or its equivalent, involving at least three or four years of intensive graduate study.

The Work of the Plant Pathologist. Plant pathologists engage chiefly in research, extension work, and teaching. Their main goal is the reduction of plant losses through accurate understanding of the disease situation and application of established control measures or the development of better ones. In achieving this objective, the plant pathologist studies both the healthy and the diseased plant; investigates the nature and life cycle of the disease-causing agent and the developmental cycle of the disease; and determines the influence of soil and climatic conditions in each type of farming area upon its intensity and rate of spread. He learns the symptoms and signs of the disease at different stages of development, the different races of the disease-producing organism involved, the comparative susceptibility of different varieties of a given plant, the methods by which the disease may be disseminated, the rates of spread and intensification under different conditions, and the kinds of plants or carrier insects which may harbor the disease and thus endanger the crop involved. He determines possible measures of prevention or control and tests them experimentally in laboratory, greenhouse, and field for their comparative effectiveness, practicability, and economy. Plant pathologists study the distribution and intensity of diseases in the field and the influence of meteorological and other conditions on their epidemiology. They study local plant-disease situations and devise control recommendations to fit the needs of each locality and crop.

HORTICULTURE

Most professional horticulturists are technically trained men who carry out experiments or investigations on problems relating to the breeding, production, storage, processing, and transit of fruits, berries, nuts, garden vegetable crops, flowers and ornamental plants, and nursery stock. Their objective in breeding is to obtain, through hybridization and selection, new and improved plant varieties that have high yield, quality, and nutritional value; are more adaptable to certain climates, regions, uses, or processes; or are resistant to specific diseases. Their work in crop production is to develop methods of growing which will insure maximum yield and highest quality. They determine the best rotation, soil, and fertilizer practices; planting methods; and spraying, cultivation, and harvesting methods for a given crop. Many horticulturists are extension workers who present technical information to the public through demonstrations, classes, and lectures; still others teach horticulture in colleges and universities.

Horticulture may be divided into five main branches, three of which are based on distinct groups of crops and two on techniques that cut across crop lines: (1) fruit and nut crops (pomology); (2) vegetable crops; (3) flowers and ornamental crops (floriculture and ornamental horticulture); (4) handling, processing, and storing of horticultural crops; and (5) nursery plant production.

Within each of these major divisions, there is a tendency for individual research workers or small groups of workers to specialize further upon a few crops. Horticulturists also specialize in some particular phase of those crops, as breeding, production, or handling.

Related Fields

Closely allied fields that are generally involved in horticultural research and practice are plant pathology, botany, plant physiology, genetics, chemistry, and soil science. Some training in these fields is essential in a sound background for horticultural research or teaching, and there is often a certain degree of transferability into or from these allied fields, particularly if additional training has been taken.

The professional horticulturist may specialize in one or more of the following kinds of work:

1. *Research,* mainly through experimentation and investigation in the field, greenhouse, and laboratory, to develop solutions to practical problems and to advance scientific knowledge in the fields of horticulture and closely related sciences.

2. *Extension* of knowledge of the field through demonstrations, lectures, the press, and any other avenues open to the general public, including direct consultation and assistance to amateur and commercial horticulturists.

3. *Teaching* in colleges, universities, or technical schools.

4. *Consulting* service, either independently or as a part of the food processing, fertilizer, or agricultural chemical businesses.

5. *Management and administration* at educational and research institutions and state and Federal service bureaus.

6. *Writing and editing* horticultural literature.

Fruit and Nut Crops (Pomology). The pomologist is concerned with any phase of breeding, growth, production, and handling of tree fruits, small fruits, berries, grapes, and edible or nonedible nuts.

Vegetable Crops. The vegetable specialist is concerned with potatoes, sweet potatoes, tomatoes, cabbage, celery, cucumbers, squash, melons, lettuce, onions, and all related truck and vegetable garden crops. Melons are generally considered fruits rather than vegetables, but because of prevalent methods of growing and handling, they are dealt with along with truck crops and by vegetable specialists.

Flowers and Ornamental Crops (Floriculture and Ornamental Horticulture). The floriculturist or ornamental horticulturist is concerned with the production of an extremely wide range of plants, having in common only the fact that they are grown because of their appearance. Some species have uses other than ornamental or landscape value, but these are not considered by specialists in floriculture and ornamental crops. Flowering bulbs, herbaceous annuals and perennials, woody flower-bearing shrubs and trees, cacti, aquatic plants, vines, shrubs, trees, and any other plant grown for ornamental use lie within the scope of the ornamental horticulturist's work.

Nursery Crop Production. The nursery business is unique in that it does not grow crops to maturity, but only propagates plants for others to grow. Most nurseries include both food and ornamental plants, trees, shrubs, vines, and even herbaceous perennials. The research, teaching, or extension work relating to nursery crops is particularly concerned with problems in propagation, nutrition, identification, and classification.

Educational Qualifications

A professional horticulturist usually possesses the minimum of a bachelor's degree in the field of horticulture or in some related or specialized branch of the plant sciences, such as botany, plant pathology, plant physiology, agronomy, pomology, vegetable production, plant genetics, or floriculture. In a very few cases, the formal professional training is more limited but is followed by progressive and varied professional experience which can be considered as the equivalent of formal education.

Foresters are concerned with the scientific development and management of forest lands and their resources, such as wildlife, grazing lands, and water; and with the use of timber for lumber, pulpwood, and naval stores, such as turpentine. Usually foresters are responsible for forest protection from fire and insect and other pests; timber management, measuring, surveying, appraising, and selling timber; range management, developing grasslands and controlling grazing; reforestation, operating nurseries and transplanting young trees; harvesting forest products, supervising logging, pulpwood cutting, and sawing of lumber; watershed protection to prevent floods and insure water supply; recreation, supervising camps in forest recreational areas; engineering of trails, roads, lookout towers, ranger stations, and telephone lines; wood technology in the seasoning, preserving, and utilization of wood and its by-products; and administration of work programs and policies.

Job Descriptions in the Plant Sciences

1. *Agrologist, Soil Mapper, Soil Surveyor.* Studies soil structure, origin, and capabilities through field trips, laboratory examinations, and controlled experimentation. Develops and carries out programs of classifying and mapping soils. Conducts investigations to determine most suitable uses for a particular soil.

2. *Agronomist, Crop-Research Scientist, Crop Scientist.* Conducts experiments or investigations in field-crop problems and develops improved methods of growing to secure more efficient production, higher yield, and improved quality. Plans and carries out breeding studies at experiment stations or farms to develop and improve varieties of field crops with respect to yield, quality, adaptation to specific soils or climates, and resistance to diseases and insect pests. Plans and carries out crop-production studies to discover best methods of planting, cultivation, harvesting, and storage of crops; soil and fertilizer requirements; and effects of crop rotation, drainage, irrigation, altitude, and climatic conditions. Develops methods and practices

for control of noxious weeds, crop diseases, and insect pests. Usually specializes in a specific crop or group of crops, or a specific agronomic problem.

3. *Anatomist.* Investigates the composition and structure of plants, primarily seed plants. Studies types, origin, topography, and structural characteristics of plant cells. Examines anatomy of leaves, roots, stems, flowers, fruits, and seed. Identifies and classifies cell types and tissue systems in vascular plants. Determines the origin and development of meristems and the primary and secondary tissues and tissue systems. Investigates the composition and structure of plants adapted to different environments.

4. *Arborist, Shade-Tree Expert.* Makes recommendations as to the planting, care, and maintenance of shade and ornamental trees. Arboriculture includes all the services involved in planting and maintaining trees, shrubs, and other ornamental plants in satisfactory health, strength, and beauty.

5. *Biochemist.* Investigates the plant biochemical reactions and factors influencing them. Studies minerals, carbohydrates, enzymes, proteins, nucleic acids, pigments, or other substances found in living plant systems. Discovers and develops the use of plant biological products in man's economy and of commercially valuable materials from items of plant biological origin.

6. *Biologist.* Performs research on the distribution, habits, life history, and classification of plants and their relationship to agriculture. Studies anatomy, heredity, development, growth, nutrition, and metabolic processes of plants. Works in laboratory, greenhouse, or field, according to nature of research.

7. *Botanist.* Studies the composition, cytology, distribution, development, environment, economic and esthetic value, heredity, physiology, and structure of plants for use in such fields as agronomy, forestry, horticulture, medicine, and pharmacy. Investigates mechanics and chemistry of plant growth, development, reproduction, and maturity. Discovers and develops both wild and cultivated plants which might prove of economic value.

8. *Breeder (Plant, Fruit, Ornamental, and Vegetable).* Plans and carries out breeding studies at experiment stations or farms to develop and improve varieties of fruit, ornamental, and vegetable crops with respect to yield, quality, adaptation to specific soils or climates, and resistance to diseases and insects. Conducts experiments to

determine the modes of inheritance of plant characteristics and develop improved breeding techniques.

9. *Certified Seed Grower.* As a member of a cooperative seed improvement association, produces and distributes pure and relatively disease-free seed of improved varieties, hybrids, or strains of such crops as corn, wheat, soybeans, oats, alfalfa, sweet clover, red clover, timothy, or other field crops in such a way as to maintain and guarantee the genetic (hereditary) identity of each lot of seed.

10. *Cotton Technologist.* Evaluates all significant factors of quality in cotton, cottonseed, cotton linters, and cotton products; relates cotton standards and other methods of quality evaluation to the performance of these products in processing and the quality of products manufactured from them. Conducts laboratory studies on the development of equipment and improved methods for determining fiber, yarn, and fabric properties, and assists in analyzing and interpreting the results of such studies.

11. *Crop Ecologist.* Studies the relations of crops to each other and to their environment, both living (*e.g.,* weeds, insects, bacteria, and grazing animals) and inanimate (*e.g.,* temperature, rainfall, and soil conditions of all kinds).

12. *Crop Physiologist.* Designs and develops research in laboratory, greenhouse, and field to advance the understanding of the growth of economic crop plants.

13. *Crop Scientist.* Plans and carries out crop production studies to discover the best methods of planting, cultivation, harvesting, and storage of crops and their soil and fertilizer requirements.

14. *Economic Botanist.* Specializes in discovery and development of both wild and cultivated plants which might prove of economic value as crops. Grows plants under controlled conditions to determine best climate, soil, and other essentials. Selects, tests, and cross-breeds to obtain optimum qualities and quantities of plants for use as foods, drugs, fibers, and other economic purposes. May explore foreign areas for plants of economic value to introduce at home.

15. *Florist Broker.* As a grower's representative to the florist trade, keeps close contact with markets within shipping range in order to supply the less congested and the best open markets. Has as his primary function the getting together of flower buyers and sellers; does not take title to goods nor physically handle the items.

16. *Florist Commission House Manager.* Maintains contact with

growers of greenhouse crops and manufacturers of florist supplies and determines the quantity and quality of materials to be handled. Is responsible for supervision of the distribution of materials handled.

17. *Florist Commission House Salesman.* Sells floral products on a commission basis to retailers. Works by personal contact or by telephone; locates special sources of supply to fill special orders.

18. *Florist, Grower Specialist.* Consults with wholesale growers, recommending changes in specific crop cultural practices when needed. Aids in solving production problems.

19. *Forest Ecologist.* Conducts research in environmental factors affecting forests. Studies biology of different species, including their classification, life history, light and soil requirements, and resistance to insects and disease. Conducts investigations and experiments to determine adaptability of different species to new environmental conditions, such as change in soil type, climate, and altitude.

20. *Forester.* Performs skilled duties of a professional nature in managing forest land. Conducts investigations on control of forest diseases, prevention of forest fires, and planting and growth of trees. Formulates and executes policies pertaining to cutting of forest trees and supervises forest areas for recreational or economic purposes. The broad area of forestry has two main areas: forest management including timber production and harvesting; and forest products utilization. Forest management may include managing watersheds; making forest inventories; surveying forest areas; reforestation; planning protection against fire, disease, and insects; managing rangelands; enforcing laws and regulations; supervising and planning logging operations; and obtaining the wood supply from large industrial holdings. Forest products utilization may include sales, research and development, or supervision in any of the industries using wood as a raw material in manufacture of lumber, plywood, pulp and paper, and silvichemicals. A few foresters conduct forest research, teach forestry, conduct forest extension work with farms and schools, or serve as specialists in range, recreation, or wildlife management.

21. *Forest Pathologist.* Conducts research on the causes of tree diseases and devises methods of control. Studies the life histories, requirements, and epidemiology of fungi, bacteria, and viruses in forest nurseries, plantations, and natural forest stands.

22. *Forestry Aide.* Assists the technician and the professional in such tasks as scaling logs, marking trees, and collecting and record-

ing data on trees; installing, maintaining, and collecting records from rain gauges, stream-flow recorders, and soil moisture measuring instruments; and serving on a road survey crew.

23. *Forest Technician.* Supervises on-the-ground operations in timber sales, recreation-area use, or research activities that require practical skills and experience; collects and sometimes analyzes and reports data within guides set up by professionals; contacts the public, contractors, and other forest users for information or policy enforcement; and supervises a road survey crew.

24. *Golf Course Greenskeeper.* Must be an agronomist who has specialized in the production and maintenance of turf. Must be acquainted with the diseases and insects likely to be found and methods for their control. Usually acts as foreman in the care of the turfed areas.

25. *Horticultural-Products Specialist.* Develops new and improved methods of handling, storage, and processing of fruits and vegetables to prevent spoilage or damage, maintain and improve quality, and increase storage life, transport range, and seasons of availability. Determines best time and method of harvesting; best types of packages or wrapping; optimum temperatures for shipping and storing; best methods of loading, precooling, and storing; effects of humidity; degree of ripeness or development in relation to flavor, disease control, appearance, and composition; and effects of treatment with gases, dips, and washes to clean, preserve, or ripen. Studies handling and storage problems in laboratory or under commercial conditions.

26. *Horticulturist.* Conducts experiments and investigations on problems of breeding, production, storage, processing, and transit of fruits, nuts, berries, vegetables, flowers, ornamental bushes, shrubs, and trees. Conducts breeding experiments to develop new or improved varieties. Plans and carries out experiments or investigations to determine best methods of planting, spraying, cultivation, and harvesting, and most suitable rotation, soil, and fertilizer practices. Develops methods of growing to insure maximum yield and highest quality. Determines best time for harvesting and optimum temperature and humidity for storage and transit.

27. *Horticulturist-Garden Store Operator.* Requires knowledge of vegetables and small and large fruits, their planting, growth, harvesting methods and marketing processes; ornamental flowers, shrubs and lawn grasses, and the basic principles of landscape design, and

the annual care of such plants. Requires business and management ability; experience in merchandising, handling of help, and meeting the public; and knowledge of accounting.

28. *Plant Nematologist.* Conducts research in study and control of nematodes (roundworms) that are plant parasitic, transmit plant diseases, or attack insects harmful to plants. Identifies and classifies nematodes and studies their structure, behavior, and distribution. Studies reactions of plants to parasitic nematodes. Develops methods and apparatus for securing representative soil samples containing nematodes, and for isolating, mounting, counting, and identifying specimens to be studied. Investigates and develops control measures. Scientists who specialize in study of nematodes that are parasitic in man or animals are classified as parasitologists.

29. *Plant Pathologist.* Conducts research in nature, cause, and control of plant diseases and decay of plant products. Studies and compares healthy and diseased plants to determine symptoms of diseased condition. Inoculates healthy plants with culture of suspected organism taken from diseased plants and studies effects to determine organism responsible for disease. Isolates disease-causing organism, studies its habits and life cycle, and devises methods of destroying or controlling it. Tests control measures under laboratory and field conditions for comparative effectiveness, practicality, and economy. Investigates comparative susceptibility of different varieties of a plant and develops varieties immune to the disease.

30. *Pomologist.* Conducts research on the physiological, biochemical, genetic, ecological, and taxonomic aspects of fruit growing. Analyzes production and cultural problems. Works toward improving methods of growing and handling fruits and nuts through research on relationships to climate, mineral nutrition, cultural practices, soil management, soil microflora, irrigation, physiological disorders, and biochemistry. Is concerned specifically with such aspects as effects of growth regulators, stock-scion relationships, pruning, fruit thinning by chemicals, fruit setting, pollination requirements of varieties, propagation, maturity, storage and handling, cultivation, and mechanical harvesting. Develops new varieties by breeding and by irradiation and chemicals, and evaluates old and new varieties. Teaches students the principles and practices used in fruit production.

Chapter XIX

Rural Social Science

Sociology is the scientific study of people living together—of people working, playing, learning, and worshiping together. Practically, sociology is used in aiding human adjustment under many different circumstances, from the family to international relations. The need for the scientific study of human relations is expanding rapidly as individuals and nations become increasingly interdependent. As the city worker becomes more dependent upon the farmer and vice versa, and as competition within and between industries continues to grow keener, knowledge to help improve personal and group relations is increasingly important.

Sociology deals with people organized in families, community groups, schools, churches, and other organizations; it studies people and groups in rural communities and their trading centers; it attempts to answer questions concerning population changes, community development, migration, job aspirations, and technical changes.

Opportunities

The demand for professionally trained rural sociologists is increasing each year. Many sources of employment are available. Colleges, universities, church groups, and government agencies including state extension services, the United States Department of Agriculture, the Bureau of the Census, and others employ rural sociologists. Industry is increasingly employing them, and various local groups are depending more and more upon them for community leadership. Foreign governments in South America, Asia, and Europe have recently begun employing American sociologists on their research and advisory staffs.

Career Areas

1. *Research.* The rural sociologist is continually pushing back the frontiers of knowledge of human behavior and social organization. Research work in rural sociology is done by universities, Federal and

state governments, and private organizations both in the United States and abroad.

2. *Teaching.* The training of future agricultural workers for better living is becoming increasingly important, and the demand for workers in this field is growing, both in high schools and colleges.

3. *Extension Service Work.* Here the sociologist is helping individuals and groups solve the problems of social and community organization in areas ranging from international programs to rural families.

4. *Survey Work.* Developing scientific and detailed information regarding any community or problem is a part of the sociologist's work. Here the sociologist may work for a local school board, a chamber of commerce, a branch of government (including Civil Service), or an industrial or professional organization.

5. *Demography.* Many rural sociologists specialize in population problems, working for the United States Bureau of the Census, the Department of Agriculture, the state agricultural experiment stations, and other public and private ventures which require knowledge of trends in population.

6. *Consultation.* Many groups and organizations employ the rural sociologist for advice on public relations, program planning, community organization studies, and public discussion of current topics.

Training

A variety of pre-professional and career courses in rural sociology are offered by many universities that offer programs in agriculture and sociology. You can choose it as a minor to supplement other professional training, or you can obtain a bachelor's degree with a major in sociology. In addition, many universities offer advanced training leading to the master's and Ph.D. degrees. For advanced students, research and teaching experience and financial aid are available through a program of assistantships and fellowships.

Job Descriptions in Rural Sociology

1. *Agricultural Missionary.* Directs agricultural education in a country unfamiliar with modern practices. Must be familiar with all types of agricultural practices and their social aspects; must possess broad practical experience in dealing with people and a knowledge of the language of the country.

2. *Farm Bureau Specialist.* Employed by a state farm bureau to promote its activities in his special field.

3. *Rural Pastor, Pre-Theological.* Prepares for work in rural community by majoring in rural sociology during pre-theological training. Prepares and delivers sermons and performs all other church duties; assists in community responsibilities. Requires knowledge of rural social problems, production management, and marketing of farm products.

4. *Rural Organizer.* Builds membership and directs educational programs for farm organizations, such as the Farm Bureau and the Grange; prepares publicity, talks before local groups, and organizes material for presentation to prospective members.

5. *Rural Sociologist.* Finds employment in teaching, research, and public and private administration of social-welfare programs. In research he formulates, conducts, and directs sociological investigations into rural life. The teacher of sociology is employed in colleges and universities, where he may take part in extension work with rural people, conducting discussions and demonstrations; he may serve as director or employee of Federal, regional, state, or local governmental units, or voluntary organizations administering social programs. In the future he should find outlets in such services as child guidance, marriage and family counseling, recreation programs, and social case work.

Appendix I

Educational Institutions Offering Instruction in Agriculture Beyond High School

This list was prepared by Dr. Henry S. Brunner, Specialist in Agricultural Education, in the Division of Higher Education, U.S. Office of Education.

Arrangement of Data

The institutions are listed alphabetically under the name of the state in which the post office is located. Branches are listed as units of the parent institution.

The capital letters "L-G" after the name of the institution indicate that it is a "Land-Grant" institution. The letters "V.T.Ed." are used to mark those institutions designated and authorized to prepare teachers of vocational agriculture for the Smith-Hughes program.

ALABAMA

Alabama Agricultural & Mechanical College, Normal. L-G; V.T.Ed.
Auburn University, Auburn. L-G; V.T.Ed.
Marion Institute, Marion.
Oakwood College, Huntsville.
St. Bernard College, St. Bernard.
Snead Junior College, Boaz.
Tuskegee Institute, Tuskegee. V.T.Ed.

ALASKA

University of Alaska, College. L-G.
—Anchorage Community College, Anchorage.

ARIZONA

Arizona State College, Tempe.
Eastern Arizona Junior College, Thatcher.
Phoenix College, Phoenix.
University of Arizona, Tucson. L-G; V.T.Ed.

ARKANSAS

Agricultural, Mechanical, and Normal College, Pine Bluff. L-G; V.T.Ed.
Arkansas Agricultural & Mechanical College, College Heights.
Arkansas Polytechnic College, Russellville.
Arkansas State College, State

Reprinted from AGRICULTURE TEACHERS DIRECTORY, 1960 EDITION

College. V.T.Ed.
Arkansas State Junior College, Beebe.
Little Rock University, Little Rock.
Southern State College, Magnolia.
University of Arkansas, Fayetteville. L-G; V.T.Ed.

CALIFORNIA

Allen Hancock College, Santa Maria.
Antelope Valley Junior College, Lancaster.
Bakersfield College, Bakersfield.
California State Polytechnic College, San Luis Obispo. V.T.Ed.
—Kellogg-Voorhis Campus, Pomona-San Dimas.
Chaffey College, Ontario.
Chico State College, Chico.
Citrus Junior College, Azusa.
City College of San Francisco.
Coalinga College, Coalinga.
College of San Mateo, San Mateo.
College of the Sequoias, Visalia.
Compton District Junior College, Compton.
Contra Costa Junior College, San Pablo.
Diablo Valley College, Concord.
El Camino College, El Camino.
Fresno City College, Fresno.
Fresno State College, Fresno.
Fullerton Junior College, Fullerton.
Hartnell College, Salinas.
Humboldt State College, Arcata.
La Sierra College, Arlington.
Lassen Junior College, Susanville.
Long Beach City College, Long Beach.
Los Angeles Pierce College, Woodland Hills.
Los Angeles Valley Junior College, Van Nuys.
Menlo College, Atherton.
Modesto Junior College, Modesto.
Mount San Antonio College, Pomona.
Napa College, Napa.
Oakland City College, Oakland.
Oceanside-Carlsbad College, Oceanside.
Orange Coast College, Costa Mesa.
Pacific Union College, Angwin.
Palo Verde Junior College, Blythe.
Palomar College, San Marcos.
Pasadena City College, Pasadena.
Porterville College, Porterville.
Reedley College, Reedley.
Riverside City College, Riverside.
Sacramento City College, Sacramento.
San Benito College, Hollister.
San Bernardino Valley College, San Bernardino.
San Diego Junior College, San Diego.
San Jose City College, San Jose.
San Jose State College, San Jose.
Santa Ana College, Santa Ana.
Santa Monica City College, Santa Monica.
Santa Rosa Junior College, Santa Rosa.
Shasta College, Redding.
Sierra Junior College, Auburn.
Stockton College, Stockton.
Taft College, Taft.
University of California, Davis. L-G; V.T.Ed.
Ventura College, Ventura.
Yuba College, Marysville.

COLORADO

Adams State College, Alamosa.
Colorado State University, Fort

Collins. L-G; V.T.Ed.
Fort Lewis Agricultural and Mechanical College, Durango.
Lamar Junior College, Lamar.
Mesa County Junior College, Grand Junction.
Northeastern Junior College, Sterling.
Otero Junior College, La Junta.
Pueblo Junior College, Pueblo.
Trinidad State Junior College, Trinidad.

CONNECTICUT
University of Connecticut, Storrs. L-G; V.T.Ed.

DELAWARE
Delaware State College, Dover. L-G; V.T.Ed.
University of Delaware, Newark. L-G; V.T.Ed.

FLORIDA
Chipola Junior College, Marianna.
Florida Agricultural and Mechanical University, Tallahassee. L-G; V.T.Ed.
Florida Christian College, Tampa.
Florida Southern College, Lakeland.
Jacksonville University, Jacksonville.
University of Florida, Gainesville. L-G; V.T.Ed.
University of South Florida, Tampa.

GEORGIA
Abraham Baldwin Agricultural College, Tifton.
Berry College, Mount Berry.
Brewton-Parker Junior College, Mount Vernon.

Fort Valley State College, Fort Valley. L-G; V.T.Ed.
Middle Georgia College, Cochran.
Truett-McConnell Junior College, Cleveland.
University of Georgia, Athens. L-G; V.T.Ed.
West Georgia College, Carrollton.

HAWAII
Church College of Hawaii, Laie.
University of Hawaii, Honolulu. L-G; V.T.Ed.

IDAHO
Boise Junior College, Boise.
Ricks College, Rexburg.
University of Idaho, Moscow. L-G; V.T.Ed.

ILLINOIS
Belleville Township Junior College, Belleville.
Centralia Township Junior College, Centralia.
Illinois State Normal University, Normal.
Joliet Junior College, Joliet.
La Salle-Peru-Oglesby Junior College, La Salle.
Lyons Township Junior College, La Grange.
Morton Junior College, Cicero.
St. Bede College, Peru.
Southern Illinois University, Carbondale. V.T.Ed.
University of Illinois, Urbana. L-G; V.T.Ed.
Western Illinois University, Macomb.

INDIANA
Earlham College, Richmond.
Goshen College, Goshen.

Purdue University, Lafayette. L-G; V.T.Ed.

Vincennes University, Vincennes.

IOWA

Burlington College, Burlington.

Centerville Community College, Centerville.

Clarinda Junior College, Clarinda.

Clinton Junior College, Clinton.

Creston Junior College, Creston.

Eagle Grove Junior College, Eagle Grove.

Ellsworth Junior College, Iowa Falls.

Fort Dodge Junior College, Fort Dodge.

Grand View College, Des Moines.

Iowa State Teachers College, Cedar Falls.

Iowa State University of Science and Technology, Ames. L-G; V.T. Ed.

Mason City Junior College, Mason City.

Muscatine Junior College, Muscatine.

Northwestern Junior College, Orange City.

St. Ambrose College, Davenport.

KANSAS

Arkansas City Junior College, Arkansas City.

Bethel College, North Newton.

Chanute Junior College, Chanute.

Coffeyville College, Coffeyville.

Dodge City College, Dodge City.

El Dorado Junior College, El Dorado.

Fort Hays Kansas State College, Hays.

Fort Scott Junior College, Fort Scott.

Friends University, Wichita.

Garden City Junior College, Garden City.

Hesston College, Hesston.

Highland Junior College, Highland.

Hutchinson Junior College, Hutchinson.

Independence Community College, Independence.

Iola Junior College, Iola.

Kansas State University of Agriculture & Applied Science, Manhattan. L-G; V.T.Ed.

McPherson College, McPherson.

Parsons Junior College, Parsons.

Pratt Junior College, Pratt.

KENTUCKY

Berea College, Berea.

Caney Junior College, Pippa Passes.

Cumberland College, Williamsburg.

Eastern Kentucky State College, Richmond.

Morehead State College, Morehead.

Murray State College, Murray.

Paducah Junior College, Paducah.

Sue Bennett College, London.

University of Kentucky, University Station, Lexington. L-G; V.T. Ed.

Western Kentucky State College, Bowling Green.

LOUISIANA

Francis T. Nicholls State College, Thibodaux.

Grambling College, Grambling.

Louisiana Polytechnic Institute, Ruston.

Louisiana State University and Agricultural & Mechanical College,

Baton Rouge. L-G; V.T.Ed.

McNeese State College, Lake Charles.

Northeast Louisiana State College, Monroe.

Northwestern State College of Louisiana, Natchitoches.

Southeastern Louisiana College, Hammond.

Southern University and Agricultural & Mechanical College, Baton Rouge. L-G; V.T.Ed.

Southwestern Louisiana Institute, Lafayette.

MAINE

University of Maine, Orono. L-G; V.T.Ed.

MARYLAND

Hagerstown Junior College, Hagerstown.

Maryland State College, Princess Anne. L-G; V.T.Ed.

University of Maryland, College Park. L-G; V.T.Ed.

Washington College, Chestertown.

MASSACHUSETTS

Cambridge Junior College, Cambridge.

University of Massachusetts, Amherst. L-G; V.T.Ed.

MICHIGAN

Alpena Community College, Alpena.

Bay City Junior College, Bay City.

Central Michigan University, Mount Pleasant.

Eastern Michigan University, Ypsilanti.

Emmanuel Missionary College, Berrien Springs.

Gogebic Community College, Ironwood.

Grand Rapids Junior College, Grand Rapids.

Jackson Junior College, Jackson.

Michigan State University of Agriculture & Applied Science, East Lansing. L-G; V.T.Ed.

Northern Michigan College, Marquette.

Northwestern Michigan College, Traverse City.

Port Huron Junior College, Port Huron.

Western Michigan University, Kalamazoo.

MINNESOTA

Austin Junior College, Austin.

Brainerd Junior College, Brainerd.

Ely Junior College, Ely.

Hibbing Junior College, Hibbing.

Itasca Junior College, Coleraine.

Rochester Junior College, Rochester.

University of Minnesota, Minneapolis. L-G; V.T.Ed.

Worthington Junior College, Worthington.

MISSISSIPPI

Alcorn Agricultural & Mechanical College, Lorman. L-G; V.T.Ed.

Clarke Memorial College, Newton.

Coahoma Junior College, Clarksdale.

Copiah-Lincoln Junior College, Wesson.

East Central Junior College, Decatur.

East Mississippi Junior College, Scooba.

Hinds Junior College, Raymond.

Holmes Junior College, Goodman.

Itawamba Junior College, Fulton.
Jones County Junior College, Ellisville.
Mississippi State University, State College. L-G; V.T.Ed.
Mississippi Vocational College, Itta Bena.
Northeast Mississippi Junior College, Booneville.
Northwest Mississippi Junior College, Senatobia.
Pearl River Junior College, Poplarville.
Perkinston Junior College, Perkinston.
Southwest Mississippi Junior College, Summit.
Sunflower Junior College, Moorhead.
Wood Junior College, Mathiston.

MISSOURI

Central Missouri State College, Warrensburg.
Hannibal-LaGrange College, Hannibal.
Joplin Junior College, Joplin.
Kemper Military School, Boonville.
Lincoln University, Jefferson City. L-G; V.T.Ed.
Moberly Junior College, Moberly.
Northeast Missouri State Teachers College, Kirksville.
Northwest Missouri State College, Marysville.
St. Joseph Junior College, St. Joseph.
Southeast Missouri State College, Cape Girardeau.
Southwest Missouri State College, Springfield.
Tarkio College, Tarkio.
Trenton Junior College, Trenton.
University of Missouri, Columbia. L-G; V.T.Ed.

MONTANA

Montana State College, Boseman. L-G; V.T.Ed.
Northern Montana College, Havre.

NEBRASKA

Fairbury Junior College, Fairbury.
Luther Junior College, Wahoo.
McCook Junior College, McCook.
Nebraska State Teachers College, Chadron.
Nebraska State Teachers College, Wayne.
Norfolk Junior College, Norfolk.
Scottsbluff College, Scottsbluff.
Union College, Lincoln.
University of Nebraska, Lincoln. L-G; V.T.Ed.

NEVADA

University of Nevada, Reno. L-G; V.T.Ed.

NEW HAMPSHIRE

University of New Hampshire, Durham. L-G; V.T.Ed.

NEW JERSEY

Rutgers, The State University, New Brunswick. L-G; V.T.Ed.
Trenton Junior College, Trenton.

NEW MEXICO

Eastern New Mexico University, Portales.
New Mexico State University of Agriculture, Engineering & Science, State College. L-G; V.T.Ed.

NEW YORK

Cornell University, Ithaca (State University of New York, College of Agriculture). L-G; V.T.Ed.

Orange County Community College, Middletown.

State University of New York. (all campuses including Cornell).

—Agricultural and Technical Institute at Alfred.

—Agricultural and Technical Institute at Canton.

—Agricultural and Technical Institute at Cobleskill.

—Agricultural and Technical Institute at Delhi.

—Agricultural and Technical Institute at Farmingdale.

—Agricultural and Technical Institute at Morrisville.

NORTH CAROLINA

Agricultural and Technical College of North Carolina, Greensboro. L-G; V.T.Ed.

Brevard College, Brevard.

Campbell College, Buie's Creek.

Charlotte College, Charlotte.

Chowan College, Murfreesboro.

East Carolina College, Greenville.

Lees-McRae College, Banner Elk.

Louisburg College, Louisburg.

Pembroke State College, Pembroke.

Presbyterian Junior College, Maxton.

(University of North Carolina, Chapel Hill) North Carolina State University. L-G; V.T.Ed.

Warren Wilson College, Swannanoa.

Western Carolina College, Cullowhee.

Wingate College, Wingate.

NORTH DAKOTA

Bismarck Junior College, Bismarck.

Devils Lake Junior College, Devils Lake.

North Dakota Agricultural College, Fargo. L-G; V.T.Ed.

North Dakota School of Forestry, Bottineau.

OHIO

Central State College, Wilberforce.

Ohio State University, Columbus. L-G; V.T.Ed.

Ohio University, Athens.

Wilmington College, Wilmington.

OKLAHOMA

Bacone College, Bacone.

Cameron State Agricultural College, Lawton.

Central State College, Edmond.

Connors State Agricultural College, Warner.

Eastern Oklahoma Agricultural and Mechanical College, Wilburton.

Langston University, Langston. L-G; V.T.Ed.

Murray State Agricultural College, Tishomingo.

Northeastern Oklahoma Agricultural and Mechanical College, Miami.

Northern Oklahoma Junior College, Tonkawa.

Oklahoma Military Academy, Claremore.

Oklahoma State University of Agriculture & Applied Science, Stillwater. L-G; V.T.Ed.

Panhandle Agricultural and Mechanical College, Goodwell.

Poteau Community College, Poteau.

Southeastern State College, Durant.

OREGON

Oregon State College, Corvallis. L-G; V.T.Ed.

Oregon Technical Institute, Oretech.

PENNSYLVANIA

National Agricultural College, Doylestown.

The Pennsylvania State University, University Park. L-G; V.T.Ed.
—Commonwealth Campus at Altoona.
—Commonwealth Campus at Behrend.
—Commonwealth Campus at Dubois.
—Commonwealth Campus at Hazleton.
—Commonwealth Campus at Ogontz.
—Commonwealth Campus at Pottsville.

PUERTO RICO

University of Puerto Rico, Rio Piedras. L-G; V.T.Ed.

RHODE ISLAND

University of Rhode Island, Kingston. L-G; V.T.Ed.

SOUTH CAROLINA

Clemson Agricultural College, Clemson. L-G; V.T.Ed.

South Carolina State College, Orangeburg. L-G; V.T.Ed.

SOUTH DAKOTA

Freeman Junior College, Freeman.

South Dakota State University, Brookings. L-G; V.T.Ed.

TENNESSEE

Austin Peay State College, Clarksville.

Christian Brothers College, Memphis.

Freed-Hardeman College, Henderson.

George Peabody College for Teachers, Nashville.

Hiwassee College, Madisonville.

Madison College, Madison College.

Martin College, Pulaski.

Middle Tennessee State College, Murfreesboro.

Tennessee Agricultural & Industrial State University, Nashville. L-G; V.T.Ed.

Tennessee Polytechnic Institute, Cookeville.

University of Tennessee, Knoxville. L-G; V.T.Ed.
—Martin Branch (Univ. of Tenn.), Martin.

TEXAS

Abilene Christian College, Abilene.

Agricultural and Mechanical College of Texas, College Station. L-G; V.T.Ed.

Alvin Junior College, Alvin.

Amarillo College, Amarillo.

Blinn College, Brenham.

Cisco Junior College, Cisco.

Decatur Baptist College, Decatur.

Del Mar College, Corpus Christi.

East Texas State College, Commerce; V.T.Ed.

Frank Phillips College, Borger.

Hardin-Simmons University, Abilene.

Henderson County Junior College, Athens.

Howard County Junior College, Big Spring.

Howard Payne College, Brownwood.

Jarvis Christian College, Hawkins.

Kilgore College, Kilgore.

Lee College, Baytown.

Lon Morris College, Jacksonville.

Midwestern University, Wichita Falls.

Navaroo Junior College, Corsicana.

Odessa College, Odessa.

Pan American College, Edinburg.

Panola County Junior College, Carthage.

Paris Junior College, Paris.

Prairie View Agricultural & Mechanical College, Prairie View. L-G; V.T.Ed.

Ranger Junior College, Ranger.

Sam Houston State Teachers College, Huntsville. V.T.Ed.

San Angelo College, San Angelo.

Schreiner Institute, Kerrville.

Southwest Texas Junior College, Uvalde.

Southwest Texas State College, San Marcos. V.T.Ed.

Southwestern Junior College, Keene.

Stephen F. Austin State College, Nacogdoches. V.T.Ed.

Sul Ross State College, Alpine.

Tarleton State College, Stephenville.

Temple Junior College, Temple.

Texarkana College, Texarkana.

Texas Christian University, Fort Worth.

Texas College of Arts & Industries, Kingsville. V.T.Ed.

Texas Lutheran College, Sequin.

Texas Southmost College, Brownsville.

Texas Technological College, Lubbock. V.T.Ed.

Tyler Junior College, Tyler.

University of Corpus Christi, Corpus Christi.

University of Dallas, Dallas.

University of Houston, Houston.

Victoria College, Victoria.

Weatherford College of Parker County, Weatherford.

West Texas State College, Canyon.

Wharton County College, Wharton.

UTAH

Brigham Young University, Provo.

Dixie Junior College, St. George.

University of Utah, Salt Lake City.

Utah State University of Agriculture & Applied Science, Logan. L-G; V.T.Ed.

—College of Southern Utah (Division of USU), Cedar City.

—Snow College (Division of USU), Ephraim.

Weber College, Ogden.

VERMONT

University of Vermont and State Agricultural College, Burlington. L-G; V.T.Ed.

VIRGINIA

Bluefield College, Bluefield.

Ferrum Junior College, Ferrum.

Hampton Institute, Hampton.

Virginia Polytechnic Institute, Blacksburg. L-G; V.T.Ed.

Virginia State College, Petersburg. L-G; V.T.Ed.

WASHINGTON

Centralia Junior College, Centralia.

Clark College, Vancouver.

Columbia Basin College, Pasco.

Everett Junior College, Everett.

Grays Harbor College, Aberdeen.

Lower Columbia Junior College, Longview.

Olympic College, Bremerton.

Skagit Valley Junior College, Mount Vernon.

University of Washington, Seattle.

Walla Walla College, College Place.

Washington State University, Pullman. L-G; V.T.Ed.

Wenatchee Valley College, Wenatchee.

Yakima Valley Junior College, Yakima.

WEST VIRGINIA

Glenville State College, Glenville.

West Virginia State College, Institute.

West Virginia University, Morgantown. L-G; V.T.Ed.

WISCONSIN

University of Wisconsin, Madison. L-G; V.T.Ed.

Wisconsin State College, River Falls.

Wisconsin State College and Institute of Technology, Platteville. V.T.Ed.

WYOMING

Casper Junior College, Casper.

Goshen County Community College, Torrington.

Northwest Community College, Powell.

Sheridan College, Sheridan.

University of Wyoming, Laramie. L-G; V.T.Ed.

Appendix II

List of National Associations

There are 2,000 national associations of business firms, manufacturers, distributors, and professional groups interested in technical and market research, sales promotion, employee training, and government and labor relations.

The following list of national associations are representative of more than one hundred organizations interested in agriculture. Many of them can provide information regarding career opportunities in the various areas of their membership.

Agricultural Aircraft Association
Chandler Field
Fresno, California 93706

Agricultural Ammonia Institute
Claridge Hotel
Memphis, Tennessee

Agricultural Publishers Association
333 North Michigan Avenue
Chicago, Illinois 60601

American Association of Nursery-men
1425 H Street, N.W.
Washington, D.C. 20005

American Bankers Association
12 East 36th Street
New York, New York 10016

American Beekeeping Federation
115 South College Avenue
Fort Collins, Colorado

American Butter Institute
110 North Franklin Street
Chicago, Illinois 60606

American Corn Millers Federation
1000 Connecticut Avenue, N.W.
Washington, D.C. 20006

American Dairy Association
20 North Wacker Drive
Chicago, Illinois 60606

American Forest Products Industries
1816 N Street, N.W.
Washington, D.C. 20006

American Honey Institute
Commercial Bank Building
Madison, Wisconsin 53703

American Institute of Banking
12 East 36th Street
New York, New York 10016

American Meat Institute
59 East Van Buren Street
Chicago, Illinois 60605

American Meat Institute Foundation
939 East 57th Street
Chicago, Illinois 60637

American Potash Institute
1102 16th Street, N.W.
Washington, D.C. 20006

American Poultry and Hatchery Federation
521 East 63rd Street
Kansas City, Missouri 64110

American Public Relations Associations
1010 Vermont Avenue, N.W.
Washington, D.C. 20005

American Seed Trade Association
Southern Building, N.W.
Washington, D.C. 20005

American Soybean Association
Box 319
Hudson, Iowa

American Stockyards Association
1028 Connecticut Avenue, N.W.
Washington, D.C. 20006

American Wool Council
Crandall Building
Salt Lake City, Utah

Association of Food Distributors
100 Hudson Street
New York, New York 10013

Bee Industries Association of America
102 Broadway
Hamilton, Illinois

California Fruit Exchange
1400 Tenth Street
Sacramento, California 95814

Chemurgic Council
350 Fifth Avenue
New York, New York 10001

Dairy Products Improvement Institute
302 East State Street
Ithaca, New York

Farm Equipment Institute
608 South Dearborn Street
Chicago, Illinois 60605

Farm Equipment Manufacturers Association
34 North Brentwood Blvd.
St. Louis, Missouri 63105

Farm Equipment Wholesalers Association
Upper Midwest Building
Minneapolis, Minnesota 55401

Garden Supply Dealers Association
Hotel Normandie
Philadelphia, Pennsylvania 19104

Grain and Feed Dealers National Association
725 15th Street, N.W.
Washington, D.C. 20005

Grocery Manufacturers of America
205 East 42nd Street
New York, New York 10017

Independent Bankers Association
Sauk Center
Minnesota

Institute of American Poultry Industries
67 East Madison Street
Chicago, Illinois 60602

Institutional Food Manufacturers Association
201 Palmer House
Chicago, Illinois 60603

Insurance Institute of America
3924 Walnut Street
Philadelphia, Pennsylvania 19104

International Apple Association
1302 18th Street, N.W.
Washington, D.C. 20006

Milk Industry Foundation
1145 19th Street, N.W.
Washington, D.C. 20006

National Agricultural Chemicals Association
1145 19th Street, N.W.
Washington, D.C. 20006

National Apple Institute
Washington Building, N.W.
Washington, D.C. 20005

National Association of Dairy Equipment
1012 14th Street, N.W.
Washington, D.C. 20005

National Association of Food Chains
1025 Connecticut Avenue, N.W.
Washington, D.C. 20006

National Association of Food Store Equipment
145 East 32nd Street
New York, New York 10016

National Association of Greenhouse Vegetable Growers
Schofield Building
Cleveland, Ohio 44115

National Association of Insurance Agents
96 Fulton Street
New York, New York 10038

National Bankers Association
P. O. Box 640
Danville, Virginia

National Canners Association
1133 20th Street, N.W.
Washington, D.C. 20006

National Cheese Institute
110 Franklin Street
Chicago, Illinois 60606

National Cotton Council of America
1018 Parkway
Memphis, Tennessee 38112

National Cottonseed Products Association
43 North Cleveland Street
Memphis, Tennessee 38104

National Council of Farmers Cooperatives
744 Jackson Place
Washington, D.C.

National Dairy Council
111 North Canal Street
Chicago, Illinois 60606

National Feed Ingredients Association
Equitable Building
Des Moines, Iowa 50309

National Fertilizer Solutions Association
Tribune Tower
Chicago, Illinois 60611

National Food Distributors
333 North Michigan Avenue
Chicago, Illinois 60601

National Food Distributors Association
12 North Third Street
Columbus, Ohio 43215

National Grain Trade Council
725 15th Street, N.W.
Washington, D.C. 20005

National Independent Dairies Association
1627 K Street, N.W.
Washington, D.C. 20006

National Independent Meat Packers
740 11th Street, N.W.
Washington, D.C. 20001

National Institute of Farm Brokers
36 South Wabash Avenue
Chicago, Illinois 60603

National Landscape Nurserymen's Association
Nicollet and Old Shakopee Road
Minneapolis, Minnesota 55420

National Lime Association
925 15th Street, N.W.
Washington, D.C. 20005

National Limestone Institute
210 H Street, N.W.
Washington, D.C. 20001

National Live Stock Exchange
Union Stockyards
Cleveland, Ohio

National Livestock and Meat Board
407 South Dearborn Street
Chicago, Illinois 60605

National Live Stock Producers Association
139 North Clark Street
Chicago, Illinois 60602

National Meat Canners Association
59 East Van Buren Street
Chicago, Illinois 60605

National Milk Producers Federation
30 F Street, N.W.
Washington, D.C. 20001

National Pest Control Association
250 West Jersey Street
Elizabeth, New Jersey

National Plant Food Institute
1700 K Street, N.W.
Washington, D.C. 20006

National Potato Council
Munsey Building, N.W.
Washington, D.C. 20004

National Poultry, Butter, Egg Association
110 North Franklin Street
Chicago, Illinois 60606

National Retail Farm Equipment Association

2340 Hampton Avenue
St. Louis, Missouri 63110

National Sales Executives, Inc.
630 Third Avenue
New York, New York 10017

National Soybean Processors Association
Board of Trade Building
Chicago, Illinois 60604

Nutrition Foundation
99 Park Avenue
New York, New York 10016

Poultry Industry Manufacturers Council
330 South Wells Street
Chicago, Illinois 60606

Poultry Publishers Association
Everybody's Poultry Magazine
Hanover 4, Pennsylvania

Society of American Florists
Sheraton-Park Hotel, N.W.
Washington, D.C. 20008

Super Market Institute
500 North Dearborn Street
Chicago, Illinois 60610

Terminal Elevator Grain Merchants Association
100 Board of Trade
Kansas City, Missouri 64105

United Fresh Fruit and Vegetable Association
Wyatt Building, N.W.
Washington, D.C. 20005

United States Beet Sugar Association
Tower Building, N.W.
Washington, D.C. 20005

Vegetable Growers Association of America
226 Transportation Building
Washington, D.C. 20006

Appendix III

Correspondence Study in Colleges and Universities—Agriculture

The following colleges offer a limited number of correspondence courses in agriculture. Address letters to: "Correspondence Study" at each institution.

Arizona, University of
Tucson, Arizona

Arkansas, University of
Fayetteville, Arkansas

Brigham Young University
Provo, Utah

Florida, University of
Seagle Building
Gainesville, Florida

Georgia, University of
Center of Continuing Education
Athens, Georgia

Idaho, University of
204 Administrative Office Building
Moscow, Idaho

Kansas State University
313 Umberger Hall
Manhattan, Kansas

Kentucky, University of
Lexington, Kentucky

Louisiana State University
169 Pleasant Hall
Baton Rouge 3, Louisiana

Minnesota, University of
251 Nicholson Hall
Minneapolis 14, Minnesota

Missouri, University of
23 Jesse Hall
Columbia, Missouri

Nebraska, University of
101 Architectural Hall
Lincoln, Nebraska

North Carolina State College
Box 5125, 1911 Building
Raleigh, North Carolina

Oklahoma State University
Stillwater, Oklahoma

Tennessee, University of
Box 8540
Knoxville 16, Tennessee

Texas Technological College
Lubbock, Texas

Utah State University
Logan, Utah

Washington State University
Pullman, Washington

Wisconsin, University of
110 Extension Building
Madison, Wisconsin

Wyoming, University of
Laramie, Wyoming

Appendix IV

Bibliography

Agricultural Engineering. The Ohio State University, Columbus, Ohio 43210.

Agricultural Engineering. American Society of Agricultural Engineers, Saint Joseph, Michigan.

Anderson, Homer Paul. *Your Career in Agriculture.* New York: E. P. Dutton and Co., Inc.

Careers in Agriculture. University of Maryland, College Park, Maryland.

Career Opportunities. Chemical and Engineering News, January, 1964. A.C.S. Applied Publications, 1155 Sixteenth St., N.W., Washington, D.C. 20036.

Career Opportunities in Agricultural Chemicals. National Agricultural Chemicals Association, 1145 19th St., N.W., Washington, D.C.

Careers in Botany. The Botanical Society of America, University of Texas, Austin, Texas 78712.

Careers in Plant Pathology. Public Relations Committee, American Phytopathological Society, Plant Industry Station, Beltsville, Maryland.

Designs for Learning. The University of Arizona, Tucson, Arizona.

Duncan, Clyde H. *Finding a Career in Agriculture.* New York: G. P. Putnam's Sons.

Employment Outlook—*Agricultural Occupations.* United States Department of Labor in Cooperation with Veterans Administration, Washington, D.C. 20225.

Employment Outlook—*Sales Occupations.* United States Department of Labor in Cooperation with Veterans Administration, Washington, D.C. 20225.

Farm Mechanic. Chronicle Guidance Publications, Inc., Moravia, New York.

Federal Career Directory. United States Civil Service Commission, Washington, D.C. 20225.

Food Industry Careers in Food Technology. Institute of Food Technologists, 176 W. Adams St., Chicago, Illinois 60603.

Girls Have a Future in Horticulture. Pennsylvania School of Horticulture, Ambler, Pennsylvania.

Hoard's Dairyman. *Choosing Your Career in Agriculture.* Fort Atkinson, Wisconsin.

Hoover, Norman K. *Handbook of Agricultural Occupations.* Danville: The Interstate Printers and Publishers, Inc., 1963.

Hoppock, Robert. *Occupational Information.* New York: McGraw-Hill Book Company, Inc.

Hutchison, Chester S. *Training for Service.* 1945 (out-of-print). The Ohio State University, Columbus, Ohio.

Keys to Careers. National Science Teachers Association, National Educational Association, 1201 Sixteenth Street, N.W., Washington, D.C.

Mightier than Missiles. American Feed Manufacturers Association, 53 W. Jackson Blvd., Chicago, Illinois 60604.

Monthly Report on The Labor Force, U.S. Department of Labor, Washington, D.C.

Morris, C. Eugene. *Counseling with Young People.* New York: Association Press.

Need a Lift?—Scholarships. The American Legion, Indianapolis, Indiana 46206.

Occupational Outlook Series, *Employment Outlook in the Social Sciences.* United States Department of Labor in cooperation with Veterans Administration, Washington, D.C. 20225.

Opportunities for Employment in the U.S. Department of Agriculture. Department of Agriculture, Washington, D.C. 20250.

Opportunities Unlimited. New York College of Agriculture, Cornell University, Ithaca, New York.

Opportunities with the Food and Drug Administration. U.S. Department of Health, Education and Welfare, Food and Drug Administration, Washington, D.C. 20250.

Out on the Range. American Society of Range Management.

Plant Physiology as a Career. American Society of Plant Physiologists, Div. of R. and O., Smithsonian Inst., Washington 25, D.C.

Rood, Allen. *Job Strategy.* New York: McGraw-Hill Book Company, Inc., 1961.

Seasonal Employment in the National Park Service, United States

Department of the Interior, National Park Service, Washington, D.C. 20225.

The Ohio State University. *Occupational Goals—Agriculture and Related Sciences.* 1945.

The Ohio State University Bulletin, 1964-65. The Ohio State University, Columbus, Ohio 43210.

There's a Future in Your Farm Background. National Sales Executives, Inc., 630 Third Avenue, New York, New York 10017.

There's a New Challenge in Agriculture. The Land-Grant College of Agriculture in each state.

Throckmorton, R. I. *Should Your Child Be a Farmer?* New York Life Insurance Company, 51 Madison Avenue, New York, New York 10010.

Townsend, Ed. *Where Are the Jobs in the 60's? The Christian Science Monitor,* 1963.

U.S. Department of Labor, *Directory of Occupational Titles, Volume 1, Definition of Titles, Second Edition.* 1949. Superintendent of Documents, Washington, D.C.

U.S. Department of Labor, *Directory of Occupational Titles, Second Edition, Agricultural Occupations.* 1953. Superintendent of Documents, Washington, D.C.

U.S. Department of Labor, *Employment, Education and Earnings of American Men of Science.* Superintendent of Documents, Washington, D.C.

U.S. Department of Labor, *Occupational Outlook Quarterly. Room at the Top for College Women.* May, 1964. Superintendent of Documents, Washington, D.C.

Veterans Administration. *Women in Employment.* Special Issue on Recruitment 1B05-174. February-March, 1964. Washington 25, D.C.

What's Ahead in Farming? 1963-64. Farm Journal, Inc., Washington Square, Philadelphia, Pennsylvania 19105.

Your Career in the Food Sciences. The Ohio State University, The Institute of Nutrition and Food Technology, Columbus, Ohio 43210.